INDIANS

POCAHONTAS, *Seymour*
SACAGAWEA, *Seymour*
SEQUOYAH, *Snow*
SITTING BULL, *Stevenson*
SQUANTO, *Stevenson*
TECUMSEH, *Stevenson*

NAVAL HEROES

DAVID FARRAGUT, *Long*
GEORGE DEWEY, *Long*
JOHN PAUL JONES, *Snow*
MATTHEW CALBRAITH PERRY, *Scharbach*
OLIVER HAZARD PERRY, *Long*
RAPHAEL SEMMES, *Snow*
STEPHEN DECATUR, *Smith*

NOTED WIVES and MOTHERS

ABIGAIL ADAMS, *Wagoner*
DOLLY MADISON, *Monsell*
JESSIE FREMONT, *Wagoner*
MARTHA WASHINGTON, *Wagoner*
MARY TODD LINCOLN, *Wilkie*
NANCY HANKS, *Stevenson*
RACHEL JACKSON, *Govan*

SCIENTISTS and INVENTORS

ALBERT EINSTEIN, *Hammontree*
ALECK BELL, *Widdemer*
CYRUS MCCORMICK, *Dobler*
ELI WHITNEY, *Snow*
ELIAS HOWE, *Corcoran*
ELIZABETH BLACKWELL, *Henry*
GEORGE CARVER, *Stevenson*
GEORGE EASTMAN, *Henry*
HENRY FORD, *Aird and Ruddiman*
JOHN AUDUBON, *Mason*
LUTHER BURBANK, *Burt*
MARIA MITCHELL, *Melin*
ROBERT FULTON, *Henry*
SAMUEL MORSE, *Snow*
TOM EDISON, *Guthridge*
WALTER REED, *Higgins*
WILBUR AND ORVILLE WRIGHT, *Stevenson*
WILL AND CHARLIE MAYO, *Hammontree*

SOCIAL and CIVIC LEADERS

BETSY ROSS, *Weil*
BOOKER T. WASHINGTON, *Stevenson*
CLARA BARTON, *Stevenson*
DAN BEARD, *Mason*
FRANCES WILLARD, *Mason*
JANE ADDAMS, *Wagoner*
J. STERLING MORTON, *Moore*
JULIA WARD HOWE, *Wagoner*
JULIETTE LOW, *Higgins*
LILIUOKALANI, *Newman*
LUCRETIA MOTT, *Burnett*
MOLLY PITCHER, *Stevenson*
OLIVER WENDELL HOLMES, JR., *Dunham*
SUSAN ANTHONY, *Monsell*

SOLDIERS

ANTHONY WAYNE, *Stevenson*
BEDFORD FORREST, *Parks*
DAN MORGAN, *Bryant*
ETHAN ALLEN, *Winders*
FRANCIS MARION, *Steele*
ISRAEL PUTNAM, *Stevenson*
JEB STUART, *Winders*
NATHANAEL GREENE, *Peckham*
ROBERT E. LEE, *Monsell*
SAM HOUSTON, *Stevenson*
TOM JACKSON, *Monsell*
U. S. GRANT, *Stevenson*
WILLIAM HENRY HARRISON, *Peckham*
ZACK TAYLOR, *Wilkie*

STATESMEN

ABE LINCOLN, *Stevenson*
ANDY JACKSON, *Stevenson*
DAN WEBSTER, *Smith*

Illustrated by Walt Reed

Samuel Morse

Inquisitive Boy

By Dorothea J. Snow

THE **BOBBS-MERRILL** COMPANY, INC.
A SUBSIDIARY OF HOWARD W. SAMS & CO., INC.
Publishers · INDIANAPOLIS · NEW YORK

With love to
Mike,
one of my favorite nephews

Illustrations

Full pages

Numerous smaller illustrations

Contents

Books by Dorothea J. Snow

ELI WHITNEY: BOY MECHANIC

JOHN PAUL JONES: SALT-WATER BOY

RAPHAEL SEMMES: TIDEWATER BOY

SAMUEL MORSE: INQUISITIVE BOY

SEQUOYAH: YOUNG CHEROKEE GUIDE

★ ★ Samuel

Morse

Inquisitive Boy

Questions!
Questions!

It was a warm, sunny day in the spring of the year 1795. Four-year-old Samuel Finley Breese Morse slid out of bed. He ran to the nursery window and peered out.

"A robin!" he cried. "Look, Nancy." He turned toward the stout figure of his nurse. "Where do robins come from in the spring?"

Nancy dipped a cloth into the bowl of warm water that stood on the low chest of drawers. She wrung it out and then dipped it into a small dish of soft soap.

"They come from the Southland, where it is warm," Nancy said. "Come here now, Finley.

Let me wash your face. It's time for you to get ready for breakfast."

"Why don't the robins stay here? *Ouch!*" Finley tried to pull away as Nancy washed his ears. "That hurts."

"They don't like cold and snow. There now, your hands and face are clean."

"Why don't robins like cold and snow?"

"It makes their noses red." She pulled the comb through his thick hair.

Finley chuckled. "Robins don't have noses. They have *bills!* And they have red breasts. Why are robins' breasts red?"

Nancy laughed good-naturedly. "So a certain little question box can ask why, I guess. I never saw a boy ask so many questions. It keeps a body busy just answering."

"I'm hungry. May I go eat now?"

"Yes." Nancy gave his hair a last pat. "And remember—no questions."

"All right," Finley promised.

Solemnly he walked downstairs and into the dining room. Dr. Jedidiah Morse and his wife were already there. "Good morning, Father. Good morning, Mother," he said.

"Good morning, Finley," said Dr. Morse.

Mrs. Morse smiled and kissed Finley on the cheek. "You look very neat this morning, son," she said approvingly.

"Let us give thanks for our meal," Dr. Morse said quietly.

They bowed their heads. When he had finished grace, Dr. and Mrs. Morse sat down, and Finley climbed into his chair.

Nancy brought in bowls of steaming porridge. Finley waited until his parents had poured cream on theirs and picked up their spoons. Then he poured cream on his porridge and began to eat.

Three spoonsful later he blurted out: "A robin! Did you see him, Father? When a robin comes, it's spring, isn't it?"

Dr. Morse laid down his spoon. His face was stern. "Children should be seen and not heard."

Finley pressed his lips tightly together for a

moment. He would not ask questions. He'd be as quiet as a mouse.

During four more spoonsful of porridge he just thought about robins. Then he piped, "Father, why are robins' breasts red?"

"Finley!" his mother said.

He pressed his lips together again. He had not meant for the question to pop out. But he *did* want to know. He liked the robins' bright orange-red feathers.

Scrape, scrape. Finley's pewter spoon had reached the bottom of his bowl. He drank his mug of milk. He wiped the whitish half-moon from his upper lip.

His father nodded at him. "You may be excused, Finley. Tell Nancy that I shall take you with me to call on Miss Russell this morning."

"Yes, Father." Finley slid down from his chair. As one foot touched the floor he turned.

"Father, why do robins hop, hop, hop?"

Dr. Morse's patience hopped, too—right out of the room! "Questions, questions questions!" he cried. "Why must you *always* ask questions?"

HOW?

A few minutes later Finley was in the nursery again. Nancy was washing his face and neck and ears for the second time. She kept an eye also on the cradle. Finley's baby brother, Sidney, lay there, kicking his heels in the air.

Nancy helped Finley put on his best linen shirt. She combed his hair again.

"Now," she said, "remember to mind your manners while you are with your father. And please, no questions."

"I'll try, Nancy."

Finley meant what he said. He would try. He liked to go with his father to visit the members of his congregation.

Finley and his father waved good-by to Mrs. Morse, standing in the doorway of their big, square house on Main Street. It was the parsonage of the Congregational Church of Charlestown, Massachusetts.

A dozen steps down the brick walk, Finley asked, "Why don't we live in a house with a porch on it?"

Dr. Morse looked down at his small, sturdy son. He smiled faintly. Sometimes he answered Finley's questions, when he felt they were thoughtful.

"Porches on houses," he said slowly, "are signs of vanity on the part of those who dwell within. We are not vain people."

"Is that why Miss Russell has a big porch on her house, Father?"

"Ahem. No more foolish questions, Finley."

A carriage drove by. The well-dressed woman who sat in it greeted them respectfully. A man riding by on a horse bowed his head in greeting. A housewife sweeping her steps looked up and said, "Good morning, Dr. Morse."

Finley felt proud. It seemed that everyone in Charlestown knew his father. He was a very important man in the town. In Boston, just across the Charles River, he was well known, too. He was a scholar and lecturer as well as a minister. And many people had studied his books about geography.

Suddenly Finley remembered something. "Will Miss Russell give us cake this morning?"

Dr. Morse frowned and said severely, "We are going to see Miss Russell to discuss the salvation of souls, not to feed our stomachs with sweets."

"But she gave us cake the last time we went to see her."

"That day it was teatime. It is morning now."

They were getting close to the town common. Finley could see the steeple of the Congrega-

18

tional Church which stood on Town Hill. Father was pastor of that church. It was a new building, for the British had burned the old one during the Revolution.

Finley could see Bunker Hill, too, and Breed's Hill, which was even higher. There the Redcoats had fought the American patriots. In that battle most of Charlestown had been destroyed. Nancy often took him for walks up there, and she had told him many stories about the war.

Dr. Morse and Finley crossed the common. Over it Paul Revere had galloped on his famous midnight ride to Lexington. Nancy had told Finley how Mr. Revere had sent a signal all the way from Boston to Charlestown, by lighting lanterns in the Old North Church steeple. Mr. Revere still lived in Boston and followed his trade of silversmith. Dr. Morse had taken Finley to his shop once. There had been so many things to look at Finley hadn't wanted to leave.

The houses near the common were bigger and finer than those near the Morse home. Some had porches and columns and flower boxes.

When they started up the walk to the handsomest house of all, Finley said, "I wish *we* lived in a place like this."

"Finley," said his father sternly, "you must not covet the possessions of others." He stopped and faced his son. "Remember," he added, "don't touch anything. Speak only when you are spoken to. And no questions!"

"Yes, Father!"

No questions! How could he find out what he wanted to know if he couldn't ask questions?

WHERE?

In the parlor of Miss Russell's big house Finley sat stiff and straight. His hands were folded on his lap, but his eyes darted about.

He wondered what kind of flowers those were, in the pattern of the silk draperies at the tall windows. Silver candlesticks gleamed on the mantel. Why didn't the pewter candlesticks at home shine like these? A soft rose carpet was on the floor. Where had Miss Russell got such a beautiful carpet? Everything at the parsonage was gray or brown, chosen for usefulness, not beauty. How nice it would be to have pretty colors around all the time!

"I see," Dr. Morse was saying, "that Mrs. Winslow is helping you now."

Miss Russell's plump, rosy face grew thoughtful. "Yes, Dr. Morse, I took her in." She sighed deeply. "It will cost a pretty penny to keep her. But we must take care of our town poor."

Finley was glad he wasn't one of the town poor. They had to work for anyone willing to give them bed and board. And he knew Mrs. Winslow had no family.

"I am sure you will be kind to her, Miss Russell," Dr. Morse said.

They talked on and on.

Finley began to squirm. He swung his legs, which did not quite touch the floor. Then he scratched his nose. He watched a fly buzz into the room and out again.

Where was the cake? Wasn't Miss Russell going to serve them any? Finley wanted to ask, but remembered: No questions.

At last Dr. Morse rose to leave. Finley slipped off his chair. Miss Russell and his father, still chatting, started into the hall. Finley followed them toward the front door.

Suddenly his nose began to twitch. What was that delicious odor? Where did it come from? Finley looked up at his father and Miss Russell. They were still talking, so he turned and walked down the hall.

At the end of the hall he peeked through a

door. It opened into the kitchen. Mrs. Winslow was stirring something in the big black pot that hung over the fire in the hearth. But the odor didn't come from there.

Mrs. Winslow continued to stir. She didn't hear him. He looked around. Then he saw another room beyond the kitchen. He could see dishes stacked neatly on shelves. That must be the pantry. Maybe the odor came from there.

Finley went across the kitchen and into the pantry. There, on a shelf, was a thick earthenware platter filled with ginger cakes.

One hand reached up. Down came a cake.

Finley didn't see Dr. Morse come into the kitchen. He was just stuffing the cake into his mouth when his father's horrified voice came from the pantry door.

"SAMUEL FINLEY BREESE MORSE!"

Finley chewed fast. He swallowed the cake before he turned around. He heard Miss Russell's tinkling laugh.

"I should have remembered how much little boys love sweets," she said. "I should have given him some gingerbread."

Dr. Morse did not laugh.

Finley felt good and bad at the same time. He knew he would be punished as soon as he got home. But he had found the source of the wonderful smell without asking a single question!

24

The Cats and Curiosity

ONE autumn morning Finley sat on the floor of the kitchen. Tiger, the family cat, sat beside him, purring contentedly. Finley stroked its fur, back and forth.

Suddenly Finley jumped up. He raced across the kitchen. As he ran out he slammed the door behind him.

Nancy watched him go. She shook her head and said softly, "That boy! He always moves as if a bee had stung him."

Two sharp, shrill whistles came from the back yard.

Nancy looked about her spotless kitchen. She

thought, "It won't stay clean long, if that signal means what I think it means. Now I'll have Billy over here, too."

She was right. In no time at all Finley was back. With him was Billy Bowen, the boy who lived next door.

Finley and Billy had been good friends ever since they were barely able to walk. They did everything together, except go to school. Finley went to Ma'am Rand's dame school. Billy's mother taught him his letters at home.

"What is it, Fin?" Billy asked. "Do you have something to show me?"

"Yes," Finley said. "That's what two whistles mean. Come over here." He went toward the cat and sat down beside it. It continued to purr. Then he began to rub Tiger's fur again, back and forth. Sparks flew.

"See!" he cried. "Almost like when we strike flint to make a fire!"

Billy dropped to his knees and rubbed Tiger, too. More sparks flew.

Finley's eyes shone with excitement. "What makes Tiger's sparks, Nancy?"

She wiped flour from her hands. "I don't rightly know," she said frankly. "But some folk say it is electricity."

"Elec—electricity?" Finley could hardly say the big word. "What is electricity?"

Nancy opened the door of the oven by the fireplace. She pushed some loaves of bread inside. Then she answered, "I heard your father say that it's something Mr. Franklin found once when he sent a kite up into the sky during a thunderstorm."

Finley thought over what Nancy had said. "In a storm there would be lightning. Is electricity something like lightning?" he asked.

Nancy sighed. "I don't really know. I guess electricity is something *nobody* knows much about." She took a last look at the loaves of bread and shut the oven door.

Finley turned back to the cat and rubbed it again. "They look to me like sparks from flint," he said. He picked up Tiger. "Come on, Billy."

"Where are you going?" Nancy asked.

"To see if we can start a fire with Tiger," Finley answered.

The boys were halfway across the room before Nancy could stop them. "Samuel Finley Breese Morse!" she cried. "Put that cat down! You can't start a fire with a cat's sparks. They're not strong enough. Besides, it's time for you to get ready for school."

Finley dropped the cat, which scurried under the table. When Nancy called Finley by his full name, he knew it was wise to pay attention. Billy, too, knew Nancy was annoyed. Quickly he headed for the back door.

Nancy looked down at Finley. "Do you know

what curiosity did to the cat?" she asked with a smile.

"It killed it," Finley answered promptly. "That's what Father says." He started from the room. "May I take the penny Mother gave me for bringing the nuts?" He had gone to the Bowens' farm with Billy and had gathered a basket of nuts.

"Yes, I suppose so. But don't lose it."

"I won't," Finley promised.

On the way to school Finley wondered about the sparks that came when he rubbed Tiger's fur. What was electricity? What did Mr. Franklin's kite have to do with it? And why was Tiger full of sparks?

IS THIS THE CURIOUS CAT?

Finley meant to go directly to school. It was a big white house on a hill just beyond the com-

mon. But he stopped to watch a squirrel leap from one tree to another. "I wonder how a squirrel can jump so far?" he asked himself.

He walked on. A fat pig waddled across the street. "I wonder why pigs eat so much? Don't they know they get killed for meat that much quicker?"

"*Chick-a-dee-dee-dee!*"

Finley looked up and finally found a small bird singing in the top of an elm tree. "I wonder why all chickadees sing that funny song? And why all crows say 'Caw! Caw!' And all——"

He stopped before a bakeshop. There was a pile of cinnamon buns in the window. "I wonder how they'd taste?"

He felt in his pocket for his penny. "I think I'll find out," he said to himself. And he went inside.

He bought two buns. He came out munching one. It was then he saw the gray cat. It was

31

walking through the dewy grass on the town
common. It crossed the street and began to
scratch at some boxes that were stacked in front
of the bakeshop.

Finley took another bite of bun. "I wonder if
it sparks, too?" he thought. "Here, kitty, kitty,
kitty," he called.

The cat turned its head and looked at him.
Finley walked over to the cat and stroked its fur.
The fur was wet with dew. It did not spark.
The cat began to scratch at the boxes again.

"H-m-m," Finley said. "Maybe this is the
curious cat Nancy and Father talked about. But,
no, it couldn't be. Curiosity killed that cat."

He took another bite of bun. "But Nancy says
cats have nine lives. Maybe you haven't used up
all of yours yet."

"Meow," said the cat.

But the cat had plenty of curiosity. It climbed
up on the boxes and peered into a rain barrel.

Then it got down and walked around the side of the shop.

Finley followed the cat through several back yards, climbing over fences. He followed it past Father's meetinghouse, through more back yards. Up a hill and around houses.

The cat walked up the steps of one house. It scratched on the door and meowed loudly. The door opened.

"Dear pussy, come in," a voice said.

Finley knew that voice. He had heard it many times before. This cat wasn't the curious cat. It was Ma'am Rand's cat!

WHAT CURIOSITY DID TO FINLEY

Ma'am Rand taught school in the big, warm front room of her house. She was an invalid and had to sit in her chair most of the time. She kept order among her pupils by using a long cane.

"Patrick Perkins, to your stool!" she said now to a three-year-old boy. He had got up to chase the cat.

There was a bowl of milk on the hearth. The gray cat had started to lap it.

Finley took off his jacket. He hung it on a peg beside the fireplace. Then he sat down on his own three-legged stool.

There were eight children in the school. Finley and Samuel Barrell were the oldest pupils. Two-year-old Patience Howe was the youngest. About all Ma'am Rand could do with Patience was keep her out of mischief.

The children sat in a half circle around Ma'am Rand. In one hand she held the cane. In the other was a tattered copy of Dilworth's speller.

"Timmy," she said, "make your manners."

A small, brown-haired boy rose and stepped forward. He stood stiffly before Ma'am Rand. His head bobbed up and down.

Satisfied, Ma'am Rand opened the speller. She pointed to a letter on one page. "What is that?" she asked.

"*B*," Timmy answered.

"What's that?"

Timmy leaned over and studied the page. He bit his lip. He shifted from one foot to the other, as he tried to think what the letter was.

"Well?"

"*J!*" he shouted, suddenly remembering.

"What's that?"

"*L*."

Timmy continued to recite. He knew the alphabet fairly well. Ma'am Rand motioned him back to his stool. She leaned over and tapped the top of Patience's head.

"Make your manners."

Little Patience made an awkward curtsy. She knew three letters—*A*, *B*, *C*. Ma'am Rand showed her the letter *D*.

"*D*," Patience said. "*A, B, C—D!*"

Then came Finley's turn. He made a deep bow. He had learned his manners nicely. He knew most of his letters. He read several sentences. He spelled seven words.

"Very good," said Ma'am Rand. And she added, "When you keep your mind on what you are doing, Finley, you do quite well."

He went back to his stool. She called Samuel Barrell. Sam was Ma'am Rand's favorite. He always had his lessons and kept his mind on what he was doing. He didn't like it when Ma'am Rand praised others for knowing their lessons. Finley stuck his tongue out as he passed Samuel. Sam tried to trip Finley.

Finley sat down. He watched the cat. *Slurp, slurp.* The cat lapped up the last of the milk. It licked its whiskers. It rubbed against Finley's leg. Then it sauntered around the room. It went toward the highboy or chest near Finley's stool.

The bottom drawer was half open. The cat put its front paws up on the edge of the drawer, and peered inside.

Finley leaned forward. The cat *was* curious, after all. Would something happen to it now? Finley held his breath.

The cat poked one paw into the drawer, and its claws caught in a half-knitted scarf. It tried to pull away, but the knitting came with it—ball of yarn, needles and all. As the cat backed away, trying to free itself, its claws made a long scratch on the front of the drawer.

"It looks like a picture of Ma'am Rand's cane," Finley thought.

Just then Ma'am Rand reached out with that cane and tapped the cat's head. The cat jumped up on the window sill.

"Finley, will you please put my knitting back in the drawer?"

"Yes, Ma'am Rand."

Finley got up and went over to the chest. As he put the scarf away, he saw a big pin in the drawer. It gave him a wonderful idea. If the cat could scratch a cane with its claw, maybe he could draw a picture with the pin. He picked it up and closed the drawer.

Finley forgot all about Ma'am Rand and school. He began to scratch the wood lightly with the pin. He stopped for a moment and looked at the marks. Sure enough, he could draw a picture. He scratched some more.

"Ma'am Rand!" Samuel Barrell cried suddenly. "See what Finley is doing!"

Ma'am Rand looked. "Samuel Finley Breese Morse!" she cried. "Come here this instant!"

Finley got up and walked slowly toward his teacher. Ma'am Rand and all the pupils stared at the chest.

"And you, the pastor's son! Give me that pin!" She took it and fastened Finley's shirt to her dress. Finley could hardly move. "Now, we'll see if you can keep out of trouble," she said.

Finley glared at the cat. Curiosity had done nothing to it. But see what it had done to him!

But it was a good picture of Ma'am Rand he had scratched on that chest. The long nose and three chins were perfect!

Fire! Fire! Fire!

SIX-YEAR-OLD Finley was taking care of his younger brothers. Dr. and Mrs. Morse had to call on a new member of their church, and Nancy had gone visiting for the day.

When Billy came over to play, Finley told him they would have to stay in the nursery. Billy found Finley sitting beside the trundle bed. His baby brother Richard was sound asleep there.

Finley held a slate in one hand. In the other he held a slate pencil. He was drawing a picture of Richard.

Sidney, who was now three, was sitting on the window seat. He was looking at a book. When

40

he came to a word he knew, he called it out so that Finley and Billy could hear. Sidney was a smart child.

Finley held up the slate. "What do you think of my picture?"

"Looks just like him," Billy said admiringly. "You're a good drawer, Fin. You make good likenesses. Are you going to be a limner when you grow up?"

"What's a limner?" Sidney asked.

"A limner is a man who draws likenesses," Finley told him.

"Are you, Fin?" Billy asked again.

"Well, I——"

Finley didn't get a chance to answer, for Sidney piped, "Father wouldn't like it."

"Oh, keep still!" Finley said sharply. Sometimes Sidney was a nuisance.

"Why doesn't he like to have you draw pictures?" Billy asked.

"Father says that anyone who has a likeness made of himself is a vain person." Finley squinted at his baby brother and sketched Richard's ear. "And vanity is sinful."

Sidney wanted to see the picture. He got down from the window seat and walked across the room. He stepped as close as he could, to see the slate better. His hand brushed against Finley's wrist.

Finley jumped. "You stuck me with a pin!"

"A spark!" Billy cried. "Did you see it? Just like those sparks from Tiger's fur!"

"I'm not a cat!" Sidney said indignantly. He stared at his finger, a surprised look on his face. "And I didn't stick you with a pin. See?" He held up his hand. There was nothing in it. "All I did was touch you on the wrist—and you jumped."

"Do it again, just what you did before," Finley ordered. He put the slate down.

Sidney backed across the room, then walked over to his brother again. He reached out and touched Finley's wrist with his fingernail.

There was a spark and again Finley felt the tiny prick.

"Ouch!" he cried. Then he laughed. "Do you suppose I have electricity like Tiger?"

"Let me see whether I can do it," Billy said. He walked across the big braided rug that covered the floor and touched Finley. Another prick and spark!

"I'm going to try it," Finley said. He reached out and touched Billy. Nothing happened.

"I'll try it on Sidney." He started toward his brother.

"No, no!" Sidney cried, and ran back to the window seat. Finley followed him across the rug. He touched Sidney's hand.

Sidney squealed, then began to laugh. "I felt it! It tingled!" he cried.

"Maybe the rug has something to do with it," Finley said. "Mother made it out of old woolen clothes. And wool comes from sheep. It grows on sheep just as fur grows on cats. Maybe that's where the electricity comes from."

Billy looked at him doubtfully. "That sounds silly," he said. "I don't believe it. But let's try it again."

Around and around the rug they shuffled, Finley and Billy and Sidney, giving one another the little shocks. "This is fun!" Finley exclaimed.

Suddenly they heard a cry outside, sharp and loud: "Fire! Fire! Fire!" A bell rang *ding, dong, ding!*

"Let's go!" Billy said.

He and Finley ran downstairs. Finley had forgotten his baby brother and the picture.

"I want to go, too," called Sidney. He had never been to a fire before.

"Hurry up," Finley said without thinking.

They ran out the front door. They raced down the walk to the gate. Not far off they could see black smoke billow up.

Billy's mother rushed by, carrying the Bowens' water buckets.

"Whose house is it, Mother?" Billy shouted.

"The Thompson house, down by the common, I think. Come, we must all help."

"Wait till I get our buckets," Finley cried.

He ran around to the back door. Beside it the family water buckets hung on a nail. They were made of leather, and the name MORSE was painted on each one. As he reached for them, he suddenly remembered Richard.

"Aren't you coming, Fin?" Billy yelled.

"I can't," Finley called. "I must stay here with Richard. Father told me to."

"Oh, he's asleep," Billy answered. "He'll be all right. Come on. Everybody's supposed to help fight fires."

Finley thought for a moment. It *was* every citizen's duty to help. Besides, he wanted to learn how the new fire engine worked. And surely Richard would be all right.

Finley took the buckets and rushed after Billy. He saw that Sidney had already gone down the street with Mrs. Bowen. "I'll have to keep a sharp eye on him," thought Finley. "I probably shouldn't let him go, either."

DOES IT WORK?

Mrs. Bowen had been right. The big, square Thompson house was belching smoke from the upstairs windows. People were running toward it from every direction. Men, women and children all carried water buckets.

"Make way for the fire engine!" someone cried. "It's coming."

Here came the bright green engine, pulled by

four stout men! They wore leather caps, with high crowns and narrow brims.

This was the first fire engine Charlestown had ever had, and it was only four months old. Mr. Moses, the blacksmith, had copied it from one used in Boston. Mr. Moses was also the fire warden in Charlestown.

"I hope I can get close to the engine," Finley thought. "Then I can see how it works."

A water lane to the nearest brook had already begun to form. Men and women stood in a line that stretched from the brook to the Thompson house. Facing them, several yards away, the boys and girls lined up. Finley squeezed in beside a big boy, right next to the house. He noticed that Sidney was farther down.

The fire engine was pulled up the water lane, close to the burning house. Now Finley could take a good look at it. It was a deep, covered tank set on a wagon frame with solid wooden wheels. A tall wooden box stood on one end of the tank, and a nozzle stuck out from the top of it. On two sides of the tank were pump handles.

The man closest to the brook quickly filled a bucket of water. It was passed from hand to hand up the line of grownups. The last one in line poured the water into the tank of the fire engine. Bucket after bucket followed. The empty buckets were handed, one by one, to Finley. He passed them on. Down the line of boys and girls they went, back to the creek to be filled again.

Soon the tank was full. Two men took hold of each pump handle. Up and down they pumped.

Swisssh! From the nozzle water spurted out in a steady stream. Mr. Moses aimed it toward a window of the burning house.

Finley watched with satisfaction. It was interesting to know how the engine worked!

Full buckets of water kept coming up from the creek. Empty buckets kept going back. *Slosh* went the water into the tank. *Swish* went the water from the nozzle, up through the window onto the blaze.

Finley thought, "If the nozzle could send the water farther, they'd put out the fire faster. Could such an engine be made?"

Finley's arms began to tire. He felt hot and dirty. But he kept passing the buckets on.

At last Mr. Thompson came to the window of another upstairs room. "Fire's out!" he called down to Mr. Moses.

"Fire's out!" went up the cry. The volunteer firemen who manned the engine pulled it away. The buckets were thrown in a big pile near the brook.

Finley ran to the pile and began to hunt. All the buckets were marked with the names of the owners. At last he found the Morse buckets. He picked them up and started for home, whistling.

He hurried. Now that the excitement of the fire was over, he began to worry about having left Richard alone. He hoped his parents weren't home yet.

Near the house he sighed with relief. The horse and chaise, which his parents used to visit people in the country, were nowhere in sight. He'd just put the buckets back and no one would ever know he had left the baby alone.

Finley went into the house. Yes, there was Richard, still asleep. But where was Sidney? Suddenly Finley remembered. He hadn't seen his brother since he had pushed his way into the water lane. He ran back outside, and to the Thompson house. A few people were still there. But Sidney wasn't among them.

"Have you seen my brother Sidney?" he asked Mr. Taylor, a carpenter.

Mr. Taylor smiled. "Last time I saw him, he was on the back of the fire engine, taking a ride."

"Oh!" Finley said. "I'd better go to Mr. Moses' shop."

He ran to the blacksmith shop. And there was Sidney, asking Mr. Moses questions about the fire engine.

Finley took Sidney's hand and led him home. As they approached the house, Finley saw the chaise. Father and Mother were back. They knew now that he had left Richard alone.

Inside, he started down the hall toward the nursery. He might as well take his scolding and get it over with.

Suddenly Sidney pushed past him. He dashed into the nursery first and told his parents all about the fire. He told how Finley had helped put the fire out. He told about his ride on the fire engine. He told how Finley had hunted for him. He told everything.

"Little helper!" Finley sighed.

Father looked grave. "Finley, you did wrong in leaving your baby brother alone, even if there was a fire."

Finley hung his head. "Yes, sir."

Dr. Morse's voice softened a bit. "But you did right in showing concern for Sidney and hunting for him."

Finley shot his brother a grateful glance.

His father went on: "And we did wrong, your mother and I, in leaving you in charge of two small brothers. You are too young for such responsibility."

Finley's spirits rose. The scolding wasn't so bad as he had expected.

Then his father looked stern again. He held up the slate. Finley had forgotten about that.

"Young man, this is no way to occupy your time. It would have been better to help Sidney learn his letters."

Finley gulped. "Y-yes, sir."

"Have I not told you often," his father went on, "that making likenesses is a frivolous use of precious moments?"

"Yes, sir."

Now Finley got a better look at the picture. He saw that he had made Richard's mouth too large and his chin too pointed. Would he ever learn to draw faces right?

"Limners," Dr. Morse was saying, "are not much better than tramps. They go from town to town, searching for people vain enough to want their own pictures. They are paid with food and lodgings and old clothes."

"Yes, sir."

"I will have no son of mine—Sidney, *what* are you doing?"

"Sparking you, Father!" Sidney cried happily. He had come up and touched his father's hand with the tip of one finger.

"How did you do that?" Dr. Morse asked.

Sidney scuffed across the woolen rug and then touched his father again. "You're full of sparks, like Tiger!" Sidney crowed.

"Ah, I see. When you rub your shoes across the rug," Dr. Morse explained, "you build up a charge of electricity in your body. Then, when you touch my hand, the charge jumps across to me. That's what makes the spark."

Finley was puzzled. "But what's a charge?"

"Sometimes," his father answered, "when you rub two things, such as leather and wool, together, electricity is built up in one of them, just by the rubbing. It is a small amount, only enough to cause a tiny shock or tingling. A small amount of electricity such as this is called a charge of electricity."

He shuffled across the rug and touched Mrs. Morse's cheek with his finger.

Mrs. Morse jumped. "Well, I never!" Then she laughed.

"Ahem." Dr. Morse drew himself up suddenly. "I must see to my sermon for Sunday." He strode from the room, the scolding forgotten.

Finley looked at Sidney affectionately. He had been a real helper!

The Amazing
Mr. Poole

DR. MORSE rattled his copy of the *Boston Gazette*. He began to read aloud, slowly and clearly:

"'Mr. Philip Poole has opened a painting room above the Flying Swan Inn, on Fish Street. The public is invited to view specimens of his art, including an amazing likeness of His Excellency, General George Washington.'"

Then he folded the paper and laid it down. He looked across the table at Finley. "You and I are going to Boston today," he said.

Finley's eyes sparkled. In all his seven years his father had rarely taken him across the river.

"Oh, Father!" he cried. "I'll get ready now!" He slid off his chair and started for the door.

"Finley! Can't you ever finish anything except those pictures you are always drawing? Come back to your breakfast."

"Yes, Father," Finley said. He sat down and began to eat his porridge.

"May I go to Boston, too?" Sidney asked. He was four years old now, and big enough to eat in the dining room. "See, I've finished my breakfast, Father."

Dr. Morse looked fondly at his younger son. "No, Sidney, not today. I must stop at the printer's to see about the new edition of my geography. There are a number of errands that I must attend to. One boy is all I can keep my eye on today."

Sidney said no more.

Finley finished his breakfast at last. Nancy began to clear away the dishes.

Dr. Morse pushed his chair back from the table. "We shall visit also the painting room of this amazing Mr. Poole." He turned to Mrs. Morse. "Finley is now seven years old. It is high time he learned how limners fare."

Mrs. Morse looked thoughtful. Then she smiled at Finley and said to her husband, "Perhaps you are right."

Dr. Morse turned to leave the room. "And when he has learned his lesson, I trust Finley will give up this drawing, on which he spends so much time. If he is to go to Phillips Academy in the fall, he should practice his penmanship."

But Finley was not listening. "I want to see that likeness of George Washington," he said.

THE FLYING SWAN

It wasn't far to Boston. In the chaise drawn by Dolly, their small, sturdy horse, Dr. Morse and

Finley crossed the toll bridge over the Charles River. They were in the city by ten o'clock.

The chaise clattered over the cobblestones to Fish Street. It was narrow and twisting, more like an alley than a street, and smelled of fish. Near by was Long Wharf. The neighborhood swarmed with sailors, rough-looking men from all over the world. Boston was a busy port.

"There it is!" Finley cried. He pointed to a faded, peeling sign that swung over a dingy inn. "There, where the man is climbing a ladder."

Dr. Morse stopped the chaise, and they stepped down to the street.

Finley looked up and down and around. He sniffed the strange smells—fish, spices, tar. He listened to the strange sounds—the tin horns and bells of peddlers, the peculiar speech of foreign sailors. He took in the new and exciting sights— the crowded street, the chimney sweep with his brooms and blanket. Charlestown and Boston were only a few miles apart. But they were as different as Finley and his brother Sidney.

"Look at that man, Father!" Finley exclaimed. "Why is he taking down the sign?"

"Probably because it is so faded. One cannot tell what it says until one is almost under it. Well, perhaps the man can tell us where to find Mr. Poole."

They waited while the shabby man climbed down the ladder. Finley was so excited he could hardly stand still. He kept looking around, afraid he might miss some new sight. What wonderful things he'd have to tell Sidney!

"Can you direct us to the painting room of one Philip Poole?" Dr. Morse asked politely.

"Indeed I can," said the man. "Follow me."

They climbed a flight of rickety stairs. The man, with sign in hand, stopped by an open door on the landing. "Come in," he said.

Dr. Morse hesitated. "Mr. Poole?" he asked.

"I am Philip Poole," said the shabby man. He laid the sign down on a rough table. He waved his hand. "And these are my paintings. Look around as much as you like."

Dr. Morse cleared his throat. But Finley was already looking about. Pictures, some propped against the walls, some on crude easels, crowded the room.

Mr. Poole began to scrape the old paint off the sign. "I have no sitters yet," he explained. "So I agreed to repaint this sign. It will pay the rent on my room for a time."

Dr. Morse cleared his throat again. He looked down at Finley as if to say, "I told you so."

But Finley paid no heed. He was too busy studying the pictures.

"Father!" he cried. "Did you ever see such beautiful colors?" He pointed to the portrait of a young lady with golden curls and big blue eyes. She seemed to be smiling at him, her lips half parted.

"She looks as if she might step right out of the picture! See, her hair is made with yellow paint, and her eyes with blue!" Finley had never seen a picture painted in colors before. He was fascinated and delighted.

"And look there, Father!" he cried. "A boy and a dog. The dog looks real enough to bark, doesn't he?"

Dr. Morse stepped closer to the painting and examined it carefully.

"Father!" Finley cried. "This must be General Washington!" He was standing in front of a large painting. Its frame was draped with a piece of faded blue velvet.

"Ah, yes, I suppose it is," Dr. Morse said. "Did General Washington sit for you?"

"No, sir, he did not," said Mr. Poole. "But I saw him once, close by. I painted him from memory. Everyone says it is an amazing likeness," he added.

Dr. Morse cleared his throat again. "Yes. Amazing," he said. He gazed at the picture. "How much do you charge for a likeness?"

"Three dollars."

"Do you have many sitters?"

Mr. Poole shrugged. "Not many," he admitted. "But I also paint signs and coats of arms. When I have no other work I paint figures in different sizes. Then when I find a sitter I just paint the face in above one of my figures. Saves time that way." Mr. Poole looked sad. "And sometimes I do house painting."

Dr. Morse turned to see whether Finley had heard. But Finley was still admiring General Washington's portrait. The eyes didn't look very lifelike, but they were a pretty, bright blue. And the nose didn't seem to come out from the face. Instead, it looked flat.

"How long will you stay here?" Dr. Morse asked Mr. Poole in a loud voice.

"Only as long as I can get work," Mr. Poole replied. "Who knows how long it will be?"

"What will you do then?" Dr. Morse asked in

a louder voice. He wanted Finley to hear Mr. Poole's answer.

"I will move on to another city or town," said Mr. Poole.

Dr. Morse glanced at his son just as Finley put his finger on one of the pictures.

"Finley, don't touch the paint! It may not be dry. Come, it's time to go."

Finley looked at his finger. There *was* a smear of yellow paint on it. He doubled his fist and put his hand in his pocket. Maybe his father wouldn't notice the smear.

"A poor and shabby profession," Dr. Morse said as they went down the stairs.

Finley said nothing. He was thinking, "I wonder where he gets his paints and brushes? I wish I'd asked him." He looked around carefully as they drove away. He wanted to remember all he could about the place where Mr. Poole had his painting room.

Soon afterward, Dr. Morse tied the chaise before a print shop.

"I must go in to discuss the new printing of my geography," he said. "In order to keep you away from the ink and the printing press, I want you to stay in the chaise. I won't be gone long."

Finley was disappointed. He had wanted to see how the geography was printed. But he settled back to wait.

He began to think about Mr. Poole's pictures. "If I only had colors," he thought, "I could paint a picture of Mother in her blue dress—or Sidney—or Richard playing with his red ball. I could practice by painting Nancy. She wouldn't mind.

"I wish I'd asked Mr. Poole where he got his colors!" Suddenly he had an idea. "If I hurry," Finley thought, "I can go ask him and be back before Father comes out."

He jumped out of the chaise. He ran down the street, around one corner and then another. He turned into Fish Street. He came to the Flying Swan Inn and hurried upstairs. Mr. Poole was still there. He had begun to paint the tail feathers of the swan.

"Mr. Poole," Finley asked breathlessly, "where do you get your colors?"

The limner looked up in surprise. "At an apothecary's shop on Old Mill Road here in Boston." He smiled as he saw the eagerness in Finley's eyes.

"Where do you get your brushes?"

"At the same shop."

Finley smiled back. "Thank you, sir," he said politely. "That's what I wanted to know."

As he turned to leave he noticed a piece of broken glass and a piece of silk and some short straws lying on the table. "Do you use these in your painting?"

Mr. Poole laughed. "No, I was trying a little experiment I heard about at the inn. It works, too. Let me show you."

Finley was all eyes.

Mr. Poole picked up the piece of glass. He rubbed it briskly with the silk. Then he held it close to a straw. The straw moved toward the glass and stuck to it!

Finley gasped. "How—why——"

"Rubbing the glass with silk," Mr. Poole explained, "makes it attract the straw. Many other substances, when rubbed, have the same power. Even the ancient Greeks knew that amber had this power." Mr. Poole talked on and on.

Finley lost all track of time. He did not hear the footsteps on the stairs. He looked up, though, in time to see his father in the doorway.

"I expected to find you here," Dr. Morse said disapprovingly.

"Oh, Father, come see this!" Finley cried.

Dr. Morse walked over to the table. Finley rubbed the glass with the silk. He showed his father how it pulled a straw toward it.

"H-m-m." Dr. Morse stroked his chin thoughtfully. "Rubbing the glass with silk makes it magnetic."

"You mean it could pick up a nail, as a magnet can?" Finley asked.

"No, it's not strong enough to do that," Dr. Morse replied. "It can pick up only light things, such as a straw or a paper. A piece of glass rubbed with silk is not a lasting magnet, either. You must rub the glass every few minutes to make it work."

"Why don't you need to rub a magnet to make it work?" asked Finley.

"Most magnets are really magnetized metal," Dr. Morse explained. "Ordinary iron and steel can be magnetized by rubbing them with loadstone. Do you know what loadstone is?"

"A heavy stone?" guessed Finley.

Dr. Morse smiled. "Most stone is heavy, but that isn't the special thing to remember about loadstone. It is a kind of black stone that is found only in certain parts of the world. The important thing about it is that, in its natural form, it attracts metal. It is a natural magnet. It stays magnetized, so it is also a permanent magnet."

"Now I understand why metal can be magnetized by rubbing it with loadstone," said Finley, picking up the piece of glass.

He began to rub the glass with the silk, but his father stopped him. "That is an interesting experiment, Finley," he said, "but we must go now."

Back in the chaise he talked to his son. "I hope you learned a lesson today. Now you see what a shiftless lot limners are. When they are not busy painting likenesses, they paint signs to hang over inns—or play at science."

Finley did not answer for several moments. Then suddenly he asked, "Father, do you know where the apothecary shop is on Old Mill Road?"

"Yes, but why do you ask?"

Finley said eagerly, "Mr. Poole said that's where I can get paints and brushes like his."

It was Dr. Morse's turn to be silent. Finley chattered on, "When we get home I'm going to ask Nancy if I may have a bit of silk I saw in her mending bag. I already have a piece of glass and I can get some straw. Father," he added, "hasn't it been a wonderful day? I learned so many things!"

Dr. Morse looked down at his oldest son. He shook his head sadly. "Yes, Finley," he said. "But not the things I hoped you would learn."

The Hare and
the Tortoise

FINLEY, who was now nine years old, sat
glumly on the back step of the parsonage. In
his hand was a sheet of paper. On it was a poem
copied from *Pilgrim's Progress.*

Finley's finger moved from word to word. He
read aloud, slowly:

> "He that is down, needs fear no fall,
>   He that is low, no pride;
> He that is humble, ever shall
>   Have God to be his guide. . . ."

His thoughts wandered. Mother and Nancy
must have that kettle almost filled with sliced

74

apples now. A clean sheet was spread out on the grass in the fall sunshine. Soon it would be covered with apple slices, drying.

Finley smiled dreamily. Apple pies! Stewed apples! Apple dumplings! Apple brown Betty! There were so many delicious things Nancy could make this winter with dried apples.

"Finley," came his mother's voice from the kitchen. "Are your brothers out there? And are you learning the poem Father gave you?"

"Y-yes, Mother," said Finley. He could see Richard playing in a pile of sand. Sidney sat on the bottom limb of the apple tree by the woodshed. He had a sheet of paper just like Finley's. On it was the same poem.

"I'll know it by heart when you get back, Father," Sidney had promised.

"I'm sure you will," Dr. Morse had answered. Then he had turned to Finley. "If Sidney can memorize it, surely, in the same time, you can."

"Oh, I will, Father." He'd work hard, Finley determined. He'd learn every word. He'd memorize it as well as Sidney, even though he wished he could go to Boston with Billy today.

Finley shut his eyes tight. He began: "He that is down——"

Finley opened one eye. He peeked at the poem, then squeezed his eyes shut again. "——needs fear no fall——"

Another peek. He lifted his eyes upward. "He that is low——"

He jumped up. "Richard, come back here!"

He laid down the sheet of paper. He was glad something had interrupted his study. He ran around the corner of the house and caught up with his youngest brother.

"Mother said you must stay in the yard." He led Richard back to the sand pile.

There Finley made a little mound. This was fun. He made another, bigger mound of sand.

"This is Bunker Hill," he told Richard, pointing to the little mound. "And this is Breed's Hill." He pointed to the big mound.

"Are you going to play Revolution with me?" Richard asked eagerly.

Before Finley could answer, the back door opened. Mrs. Morse came out, carrying a kettle. It was filled with fresh apple slices.

"You play Revolution, Richard. You can use sticks for soldiers." Finley ran over to Mrs. Morse. "May I help spread the apples, Mother? May I?"

She smiled at his eagerness. "If you think you can do that and still memorize the poem, you may."

"Oh, yes, Mother, I can do both."

Together they spread the apple slices out on the clean sheet. They were careful that none of the slices overlapped others. All of them must dry evenly.

"Why do you dry apples?" Finley asked when they had finished.

"So we will have fruit to eat all winter," Mrs. Morse said. "Fresh apples, even when kept in the cellar, get soft and mushy before spring. The dried apples keep without spoiling. Now, better get busy on your poem." She went back into the house.

Finley looked at Sidney. He was still sitting up in the apple tree. He was staring straight

ahead, while his lips moved soundlessly. He would be sure to know the poem when Father came home. Finley started back to the step and his sheet of paper.

BY THE WAYSIDE

"Look what I found!" Richard cried. "In the sand pile, at the bottom of Bunker Hill." He held out a small chunky object, covered with dirt.

"It's a bullet," Finley said. "Let me see it."

"You can have it," his brother said. "I must get back. The Redcoats are coming up the hill." He hurried to the sand pile.

Finley took the bullet eagerly. Dozens like it had been found in the neighborhood. Ever since his visit with Mr. Poole, Finley had taken a new interest in all objects. It was fun to test them for magnetism. Could he make the bullet magnetic?

He reached in his pocket and pulled out a piece of silk. He rubbed the bullet, then held it close to a dandelion puffball in the grass at his feet. Nothing happened.

Maybe the fuzz was stuck too tight to the stem. He picked the dandelion and blew some of the fuzz onto his hand. Then he rubbed the bullet again and held it close to the fuzz. Still nothing happened.

"I can't magnetize it by rubbing it," he thought. He had rubbed so many things with silk. He had rubbed a bone. Nothing had happened. He had rubbed a pewter spoon. Nothing had happened. Why did rubbing magnetize some things and not others?

"I wish I had a piece of amber or jet or——"

His wish was interrupted by two sharp whistles.

"Billy!" he thought happily. "I hope he's brought my paints." Finley stuffed the bullet and the piece of silk in his pocket and ran to the fence. He jumped over it lightly.

"Did you get them, Billy?"

Billy handed Finley a small parcel.

"Are my paints in here?" Finley asked in amazement. "Let's see what they look like." He opened the parcel. "Why, there's nothing but some old brown powder!"

"That's powdered burnt sienna," Billy said. "It makes brown paint. All the colors were powdered."

"*All* the colors! This is only brown. Where are the other colors? Red and yellow and blue?"

"There wasn't enough money. The apothecary said the colors come from all over the world. They're very expensive. Burnt sienna was the cheapest he had."

Finley thought of how long he'd saved to buy paints. Father gave him a penny a week to drive the cow to pasture. And Grandfather Morse had

given him some pennies on his birthdays. All
this he had saved and given to Billy to buy the
paints for him.

Finley was much disappointed. Then he
brightened. "Well, I can paint a brown picture.
Come on, let's go over to my yard."

The boys jumped over the fence.

"Wait here on the step," Finley said. He ran

into the house and upstairs to his own room. Mother and Nancy were peeling apples and talking in the kitchen. They did not hear him. He came back with a smooth board and sat down on the step.

"See—" he showed it to his friend—"I drew a picture of Nancy here with charred wood. Now I'm going to paint it." He thought for a moment. "Nancy has brown eyes, and she almost always wears a brown dress. Maybe the picture won't look too bad."

"How are you going to paint with powder?"

"I'll have to mix it with a liquid."

Finley thought. Water? That didn't sound right. Milk? No. Then he remembered Mr. Poole had talked about *oil* painting. Yes, that was it! Where could he get some oil? Suddenly he jumped up.

"Castor oil!" he shouted and ran quickly into the house.

"Castor oil?" Billy echoed. But Finley had already disappeared. In a moment he was back, holding a bottle and a cup.

"Are you going to mix the powder with *castor oil?*" Billy wrinkled his nose.

"It's oil, isn't it? And I'm supposed to use oil." Finley put the powdered burnt sienna and some castor oil in the cup and mixed them into a paste. "It doesn't smell very good, but I think I can make it work."

He picked up a small stick, dipped it into the paste and began to paint in Nancy's picture. It was all brown, but it looked more like Nancy than the charcoal outline had.

"Just think of the pictures I could paint if I had all the colors!"

Billy watched with admiration. "I wish I could paint," he said.

Just then they heard the sound of horse's hoofs. Father was home!

"It must be dinnertime," Billy said. "I'll see you tomorrow."

Sidney climbed down from the apple tree. He ran toward Dr. Morse. "Father!" he shouted. "I've memorized the poem."

Finley's heart sank. He hadn't learned a single line of the poem.

"YOU'RE LIKE THE HARE, FINLEY"

Father saw the picture of Nancy as he approached the house. "So you have been busy, Finley," he said. He sniffed. "That smells like castor oil. Has someone been ill?" He picked up the earthenware cup and sniffed again.

"No, sir, Father, I—uh—I mixed my color with castor oil so I could paint."

"Did you find time to memorize the poem?" Dr. Morse asked.

"No, sir." Finley hung his head.

"As usual, I suppose, your attention was attracted to other things," Dr. Morse said.

Mrs. Morse appeared in the doorway. "I was partly to blame," she said. "I shouldn't have let him help me spread out the apples."

"Oh, no, Mother," Finley protested. "It was just that I—uh——"

Dr. Morse waved his hand. "I am sure that if Finley hadn't spent that time helping you he would have found something else to distract him. Come, boys, into the study. I want to see how you've done."

They followed their father.

Sidney rattled off the poem without a mistake.

"Do you know any of it, Finley?" his father asked.

Finley tried. He got as far as "He that is down——"

His father looked at him thoughtfully. Then he drew both boys onto his knees.

"Finley," he asked, "do you remember the fable of the Hare and the Tortoise?"

"Oh, yes." Finley had always liked to read stories. "They had a race. The Tortoise won, even though he moved much more slowly than the hare."

"Why did he win?" asked his father.

"Why, because the Hare stopped so many times to take naps," Finley said. "And the Tortoise kept on going and passed him while he was sleeping."

"That is correct," Dr. Morse said. "And do you know, Finley, you and Sidney remind me very much of the Tortoise and the Hare?"

Both boys looked puzzled. "We do?" Finley said. "Why?"

Dr. Morse drew Sidney a little closer to him. "Sidney," he said, "is like the Tortoise. He is slow, but he moves forward steadily. He sets himself a goal and keeps going toward it until he reaches it."

The arm about Finley's shoulder tightened.

"You, Finley, are like the Hare. You move swiftly. But you stop by the wayside so much—

not to sleep, you understand, but to examine everything you see. That is why, in memorizing the poem, the Tortoise, or Sidney, passed you."

Finley hung his head again. Father was right. Dr. Morse handed the paper back to Finley. "Keep on working," he said. "But this time stick to the task until you have finished it."

"Yes, Father."

Finley went outside and picked up the picture of Nancy. He took it into the kitchen and gave it to her.

She beamed with pleasure. "Why, it really looks like me!" she said. "May I keep it?"

"If you want it," Finley said.

"How nice of you, Finley!" His mother smiled.

Back on the step he sat down again. He studied the poem. He closed his eyes and repeated: "He that is down, needs fear no fall——"

Finley opened his eyes. He couldn't think of the next line. All he could think of was that Nancy had said the picture looked like her. Maybe he *would* be a limner someday!

Then he remembered what his father had told him about the hare. "But if I didn't stop by the wayside," he thought, "I'd miss so many things!"

The Talking Mill

ONE FINE September morning Finley sat under the old apple tree in the yard. He was whittling on a toy boat for his brother Richard. Sidney was up in the apple tree, reading. Mrs. Morse was busy in her herb garden.

There was a sound of horses neighing. Finley stood up and looked over the fence. Billy and his father were hitching up their farm cart. Then Mr. Bowen and Billy came over to the Morses' back yard.

"Mrs. Morse," Mr. Bowen said, "I am driving out to my father's farm to help with the harvest. Billy wants Finley to go along with us."

Mrs. Morse straightened up. She saw Finley watching hopefully. She smiled at him and turned to Mr. Bowen. "Yes, he may go."

Finley dropped the toy boat and put his jack-knife in his pocket. A trip to the Bowen farm! What fun he and Billy would have in their secret cave along the brook.

"May I go, too?" Sidney asked as he dropped down from his perch in the apple tree.

"You may if your mother doesn't care," Mr. Bowen said.

"Does he have to go?" Finley asked sadly.

Mrs. Morse nodded. "Of course Sidney may go. Nancy and I will be busy all day making candles. We'll have Richard to look after. You must not be selfish, Finley."

"It isn't that, Mother. But Sidney is so slow. We'll be waiting for him all the time."

He added to himself, "We'll have to let him go with us to our secret cave on the farm."

"You must take Sidney along," was his mother's firm answer.

A few minutes later Finley and Sidney were riding beside Billy in the back of the cart. Large, billowy clouds hung in the sky. Great elms and oak trees spread their branches out over the dusty road.

The cart forded a creek. "Look at the birch trees!" Finley cried. "I wish I were an Indian and had a birchbark canoe!"

"If I were an Indian, I'd go hunting with a bow and arrow," Billy said.

"I'd go on the warpath," Sidney declared.

"Ha, you wouldn't get very far," Finley said. "Besides, you're only six years old. You'd better leave the men's work to Billy and me. We're both nine."

Mr. Bowen turned the cart into a lane and drew up to a farmhouse.

"I'm glad you came," Billy's grandfather

greeted them, as they climbed out of the cart. "I need plenty of help."

"That's why I brought the boys," Mr. Bowen said. "They can pick up the turnips as I dig them."

The boys followed Mr. Bowen to the turnip field. For a while it was easy to shake the dirt off the vegetables and drop them into baskets. But the boys soon grew tired. Helping Mr. Bowen was harder work than they had expected.

Finally they reached the last row. "You boys can take a look around the farm now," Mr. Bowen said.

"Hooray!" Billy shouted, his tiredness forgotten. "Let's go to the barn!" He and Finley ran toward the farm buildings.

"Wait for me!" Sidney cried.

"Tortoise," Finley said disgustedly. "That's a good name for him."

They went into the barn, climbed into the

95

haymow, slid off the hay to the dirt floor. Out the barn door. Into the well house. Out again. Into the springhouse and out.

"Wait for me!" Sidney cried, again and again.

Suddenly Finley skidded to a stop behind the barn. He went up to a big hollowed-out tree stump half hidden in a clump of dry weeds. There was a hole in the center of the stump.

"What's this, Billy?"

"A hollow stump. Can't you see?"

"Yes, but it didn't grow like this. Someone must have made it."

"I don't know," Billy said. "There's Grandfather over by the barn. I'll ask him."

The old man had heard the boys. He walked over and said, "I'll tell you what that is. It's what's left of our sweep-and-mortar mill."

Finley looked puzzled. "A sweep-and-mortar mill? What's that?"

"Yes." Then Grandfather Bowen explained.

"It was used for grinding corn when I was a boy. You put the dry kernels in the hollow of the stump and fastened a kind of club, or pestle, with leather thongs to a sampling. Then you pulled the pestle down hard to pound the corn. The sapling was like a spring. It helped lift the pestle up again. Up and down, up and down, you moved the pestle until the corn was pounded as fine as you wanted it."

Mr. Bowen's faded eyes twinkled. He pointed to a tree near by. "When I was a boy that tree," he said, "was the sapling to which my father tied the pestle. It has grown some since."

Finley looked at the hollowed-out stump to imagine how the pestle pounded the corn. "This is certainly different from the big gristmill, with a stream turning the wheel," he said. "Gristmills grind the corn much faster and easier."

The old man stroked his chin. "But you can't talk to your neighbor with a gristmill."

Finley's eyes grew wide. "You mean neighbors used to talk to each other with these mills?"

"In a way, yes," Grandfather Bowen replied. "Of course, they couldn't carry on long conversations, but they could send short messages. Billy, run up to the barn and get that rope hanging inside the door. I'll show you how my mother used to call us to the house when we were out in the woods or fields."

The boys were eager to help. Billy got the rope. Finley cleaned some of the dirt and twigs out of the stump. Grandfather Bowen cut a limb to make a strong, new pestle. He fastened it to another sapling. Then he brought it down hard in the tree stump.

Boooom! the sound went across the fields. Up, and down again: *Booooom!*

"Why, you could hear that clear to Concord!" Billy cried.

"Not quite that far," Grandfather Bowen said,

"but the sound carries several miles. When my mother wanted us to come to the house, she always hit the stump once with the club. If she needed help, she'd hit the stump twice."

"Just as we whistle to each other!" cried Billy. "Only in our code two whistles mean one has something important to show or tell the other."

"And three whistles mean that all is safe," Finley said.

Grandfather Bowen nodded. "Messages have been sent by codes and signals for a long time. Indians, you know, talked to one another with smoke signals."

"And sailors signal to other ships with flags," Sidney said.

"I know what we can do," Finley said. "Billy and I will go down to the brook in the woods. We'll mark our trail as the Indians used to do. Sidney, you see whether you can follow us."

"That will be fun," Sidney said.

BOOM! BOOM! BOOM!

"He's so slow he'll never catch up with us," Finley said a few minutes later. He stooped down and put one stone on top of another, then another stone to one side. "We can play by ourselves in the cave for an hour before he gets down here."

They left the path and went through a small grove. They bent several twigs to show which way they had gone. They reached the brook. Finley led the way to their cave in the bank.

"Are you going to let Sidney know where our cave is?" Billy asked.

"No, I won't put any markers on this side of the brook."

"What will he do when he gets to those last stones and can't find us?"

"He'll probably hunt around, then sit down and wait for us. Come on, we'll pretend we're American soldiers fighting off Redcoats."

100

They played in the cave a long time. Then
Billy said, "We'd better get back for dinner."

They ran to the place where they had put the
last three rocks. Sidney wasn't there. He wasn't
anywhere around.

They hunted for him up and down the brook.
They waded back and forth across the brook and
hunted for him on either side. But not a sign
of the little boy could they find.

"Maybe he just wandered off into the woods," Finley said hopefully.

He and Billy called. There was no answer.

"He may have gone back to the house," Billy suggested.

They went back to the farmhouse. Mr. Bowen joined in the search. So did Grandmother and Grandfather Bowen.

"Maybe he was angry and started back home on foot," Billy said suddenly.

"He might have," said Mr. Bowen. "Finley, suppose you start walking back to Charlestown. If he started home by himself, perhaps you can overtake him. I'll search the woods again."

"I should be able to catch up with him," Finley replied. "Sidney is so slow."

Then he wished he hadn't said that. He wished he hadn't been impatient with his little brother. If only he could find Sidney, he'd never tease him again.

Finley ran down the road toward home. He strained his eyes for a small figure trudging ahead. He ran and ran. He could hardly get his breath. But there was no sign of Sidney.

He was almost halfway to Charlestown. His heart was heavy. He would have to go home and tell his parents——

Boom! Boom! Boom! The sound came through the crisp fall air.

Finley stopped in his tracks. "The sweep-and-mortar mill!" he exclaimed. Why would anyone play with it when Sidney was lost? But maybe it wasn't play. Maybe it was a real signal!

Boom! Boom! Boom!

There it was again. It must be a signal. Three whistles meant all was safe. Then three booms must mean the same thing. Sidney! They had found Sidney!

Finley raced back to the Bowen farm. When he got to the house, he was so tired he could barely walk. And there was Sidney, safe and sound, talking with the others.

"He was up in the hayloft, playing with the kittens," Billy said.

"But, Sidney," Finley cried, "didn't you hear us calling you?"

"Um-hum," Sidney answered.

"Why didn't you answer?"

"Didn't want to," Sidney replied. "You played a trick on me and I played a trick on you."

"Serves me right," Finley said sheepishly.

"Could you hear the sweep-and-mortar mill?" Billy asked after a moment's silence.

"Yes, and I was glad to get that message," Finley answered.

Grandfather Bowen chuckled. "Now you understand why we used to say the sweep-and-mortar mill was as good for talking as for grinding corn. Sometimes a message can be even more important than food."

Invisible
Message

TEN-YEAR-OLD Finley brought the ax down, hard. *Crack!* The chunk of wood split straight down the center. He took the two pieces and threw them on a small pile near by.

Billy picked up pieces from the pile. He stacked them on his left arm. Out of the corner of his eye he watched Finley. There was a pleased look on his face.

Finley stopped splitting wood. He leaned the ax against the woodshed. He thrust his hand into his pocket and drew out a sheet of paper.

"Billy," he said, for the third time, "are you sure you wrote something on this?"

"Yes," Billy answered solemnly. "I'm sure. It's just invisible, that's all." He grinned gleefully. "Give up?"

"No, if there's a message on this paper I'll find a way to make it visible—all by myself." Again he held it up to the light. He could see nothing on it.

"Hmph," he snorted in disgust and put it back in his pocket.

The ax went up and down again. Billy took a load of wood into the parsonage kitchen. He was helping Finley fill the woodbox for Nancy, just as Finley often helped him fill the Bowens' woodbox.

As Finley worked he kept thinking about the piece of paper. Billy had brought it over to his house a short time ago. He had said that Finley could never make the message written on it visible. It was a challenge that Finley could not turn down.

106

Suddenly he sat down on the grass. He took the paper out again and rubbed it with his finger. He could feel nothing on it.

He heard Billy slam the kitchen door. Hastily he stuffed the paper back into his pocket.

"Give up?" Billy asked again.

"No." Finley rose and picked up the ax. *Crack* went another piece of wood. Billy started to collect another load.

"Well, I hope you'll find out soon how to read that message. Then we'll be able to write messages to each other before you leave for Phillips Academy."

"I'll find out," Finley said. "I'll be just as glad as you when we can read messages that prying Sidney can't read."

"He must have found out we put notes in the hollow tree by the pasture. If he hadn't seen your note yesterday, he wouldn't have known you'd asked me to go fishing today."

"If he hadn't followed us," Finley said, "and made so much noise, the fish wouldn't have been scared away."

"And it does no good to change hiding places. He always finds them right away. Of course—" Billy grinned as he started for the kitchen again—"we could just tell each other these things. Then he wouldn't find out what we're going to do."

"Sending messages is lots more fun," Finley said, smiling too.

He took the paper out again. He rubbed it. He held it up to the light. He breathed on it. He shook it.

Billy chuckled as he came back. "Give up?"

Before Finley could answer, they heard Mrs. Bowen's voice come clearly through the twilight. "Bill-y-y! Supper's ready!"

"Coming, Mother." And away he went.

Finley put the paper into his pocket. He

picked up an armful of wood and carried it into the kitchen.

Perhaps if he rubbed the paper with a piece of silk, something would happen, but it didn't.

He scowled. "I won't give up," he said to himself. "I'll find out how to make that message visible before I go to Andover even if it takes every day of the next two weeks."

BY ACCIDENT

The next morning Nancy brought two pails full of milk into the kitchen. She set them on a low bench.

"Time to take the cow to pasture, Finley."

He nodded and went out. He headed for the cowshed. It stood in the shade of one of the gnarled old apple trees at the rear of the parsonage property.

He let down the bar of the shed and let Old

Bess out. He drove her down the path that ran along the back of the Bowens' place.

He stopped and gave a long, loud whistle, but Billy did not come out the kitchen door. He whistled again and called, "Billy." There was no answer.

A puzzled frown came to Finley's face. Billy hadn't said anything about going away this morning, but there didn't seem to be anyone at home to answer the call.

"Oh, well, Bess," said Finley good-naturedly, "we'll just have to go to pasture by ourselves today."

He patted his pocket. "It will give me time to figure out this message without Billy saying 'Give up?' every few seconds."

He went on talking to the cow. "If I gave up and asked him how he wrote it and how I could read it, I'd never hear the last of it."

Old Bess eyed him. "Moo!" she said.

Finley grinned. "I knew you'd understand." And they went on to the pasture.

They reached a meadow which sloped gently toward a brook. Several Charlestown families kept their cows here. Finley saw the Bowen cow was already in the pasture. He recognized its brown-and-white markings at once. "The Bowens left early this morning, all right," he thought. "I wonder where they went?"

Then he remembered the hole in the old oak tree at the edge of the pasture. It had been a good place to leave messages until Sidney had found it.

"Maybe Billy left a note there," he thought. "And Sidney couldn't have got here ahead of me this morning."

Finley raced to the tree. He poked his arm into the hole. His fingers closed around a piece of paper. Hastily he drew it out and opened it. It was blank.

111

"Another invisible message," he thought. He put it in his pocket with the other one.

Back at home, in the kitchen, he pulled the papers out again. He looked at them and tried to think of a way to make the messages visible.

One of the papers slipped out of his hand. It floated down to the hearth, to the edge of the fire. Finley knelt down to get it. The paper was turning toast-brown. He looked more closely. Something else was browner! The message!

Going away, he read in his friend's handwriting on the brown paper.

Excitedly Finley fished the paper from the fire. "Heat!" he murmured. "That's what it needs to make the writing show." He took out the other message and held it close to the fire. In a few seconds the words *To Boston* appeared.

Finley rocked back and forth on his heels and smiled in triumph. He had discovered one of the secrets—even though it had been by accident!

NEVER SATISFIED

Finley was impatient for his friend to return. But while he waited he experimented in his room with messages. "Now what did Billy use to write with?" he asked himself. "It had to be some kind of liquid. But what?"

Finley thought hard. "It was a liquid that doesn't show when it's dry. Water?"

He tried writing with water. When dry, his message didn't show. He held it close to the flame of a candle. It didn't show then, either.

He tried castor oil. It showed on the paper both before it was dry and afterward.

He got some egg white from the kitchen. It didn't work either. Restlessly he went back downstairs. Nancy was cooking dinner. She had to heat some milk in a pan over the coals of the fire. She asked him to hold the pan.

"Watch it carefully," she added. "Milk burns so easily."

Finley didn't take his eyes off it. Just as the milk started to bubble up the sides of the pan it turned brown. He almost dropped the pan in the fire. Had Billy used milk to write that message? "I'll have to test it," Finley thought.

He handed the pan to Nancy, and asked if he might have some of the milk. Nancy shook her head, puzzled, but poured a little into a cup.

Finley ran upstairs to his room. He grabbed a piece of paper. He dipped one finger into the milk. Carefully he wrote his initials on a sheet of paper.

He blew on it to make them dry faster. The milk didn't show. Excitedly he lighted a candle, and held the paper close to the flame. Slowly the letters S F B M turned brown. It was easy to read them.

Finley laughed happily. He had solved the mystery at last!

That afternoon, when the Bowens returned home, Finley was waiting in the yard. "You've been to Boston!" he cried, as Billy leaped out of the chaise. "I know! I read your message!"

Billy looked a bit crestfallen. "I thought I couldn't fool you for very long, Fin." Then he brightened. "Well, it looks as though I won't be lonesome here after all, when you go to the academy at Andover."

"Why?"

"Because today Father took me to Mr. Cox, a printer in Boston. And he signed the papers to make me an apprentice."

"That means you're going to learn the printer's trade!" Finley cried. "How wonderful!"

Billy nodded. "I'm glad about it. It's a good trade. But say, how did you figure out the invisible messages?"

Finley's face flushed. "Well, I wasn't going to let you know, but it was by a kind of accident." He told Billy how the paper had fallen near the fire. "And I found out what you wrote it with, too. Milk!"

Billy looked at him admiringly. "You're never satisfied, are you, Fin, until you learn all there is to know about something like that?"

The Academy
at Andover

FINLEY's voice rose in song, loud and shrill:
" 'Oh, dear, what can the matter be?' "

Samuel Barrell, his roommate, laughed.

Finley turned away. Determinedly he looked
out the window. Just below was the meadow
behind the dormitory of Phillips Academy at
Andover. He sang on: " 'Oh, dear, what can the
matter be?' "

Horace Hill, another roommate, howled with
laughter. "What can the matter be? Your singing, that's what!"

Finley clenched his fists. " 'Oh, dear, what
can the matter be?' "

"Who let the cat out?" yelled Lionel Dexter, his third roommate. "Meow!"

Ever since Finley had started practicing the song a week ago, the boys had tormented him. Every boy in the academy had to take singing lessons. Finley was one of three chosen to sing a solo on Exhibition Day. The program was just three days from now. And Dr. Morse was to make the Exhibition Day address!

Finley already knew the song. But the singing teacher said he must practice it anyway. He must learn to pronounce each word just so and to sing each note exactly right.

Finley turned and faced the boys defiantly. " 'Johnny's so long at the fair.' "

All three roommates doubled up and guffawed. Finley could stand it no longer. He made a lunge for Samuel Barrell, who was nearest him. He caught Samuel off guard and knocked him backward. The boys rolled off the cot, laughing. They hit the floor with a crash. Soon they were a tangle of arms and legs.

Finley had not seen the tall figure standing in the doorway. He did not see Master Newman stalk across the room. But he did feel a firm hand on his collar. He felt himself jerked to his feet. And his ear rang with the slap he received.

"I have had enough trouble from you, young man," Master Newman said. And he gave Finley a good tongue-lashing about his idleness and his failure to study hard enough.

Finley tried to stifle his anger. It was boiling when the master turned and left. It was still boiling that night, when the candles were snuffed in the dormitory.

For the second time since he had come to Andover he got out of bed in the middle of the night. He slipped on his clothes, careful not to waken the other boys. He grabbed a jacket and tiptoed noiselessly out of the room.

Down the corridor he crept, and out the front door. He slipped from the shadow of the building into the shadow of the bushes. At last he reached the road that ran past the academy.

It was twenty miles to Charlestown. But Finley did not think of the distance as he trudged down the road. He was eleven years old, and husky. He thought only of getting home as quickly as possible.

Dawn came. From a side road a cart full of vegetables turned into the highway. The driver was an old man. "Going far, lad?" he asked.

"I'm going to Charlestown, sir."

"Hop on and ride with me." The old man smiled. " 'Tis a long ride to market without someone to talk to."

Finley chatted the rest of the way. If the old man suspected him of being a runaway he gave no sign. He seemed too glad to have company to ask questions.

It was almost noon when Finley arrived home.

"So you have run away again?" Dr. Morse said sternly as Finley walked in. "What was the trouble this time?"

Finley told him all about the tussle and Master Newman's slapping him.

"You must learn to control your temper, Finley," his father answered. "Tomorrow you must go back to school."

PEACE PIE

Early next morning Finley climbed into the chaise beside his father. His face was glum as he settled back in the seat.

The door of the parsonage opened. Mrs. Morse came out, a parcel in her hands. She carried it carefully to the chaise and smiled up at Finley.

"Here is a pie that Nancy baked for you this

morning. Good-by, son. Your father and I will be up Friday for the Exhibition Day program."

"Good-by, Mother." Finley smiled then. He felt a little better. He waved at his mother until he could see her no more.

He shouldn't have run away from school. He knew that. His parents had scolded him, but they had also promised him treats to make his stay in Andover easier. They had agreed he could come home every other week end. Thinking of this, Finley decided he must show them his gratitude. He must be able to sing his song perfectly on Exhibition Day.

That afternoon he practiced again: " 'Oh, dear, what can the matter be?' " His voice cracked on the last note.

"I can't sing!" he wailed. "I sound like a frog with a boy in its throat."

"You sound worse than that," Samuel said unfeelingly. "I'm glad I don't have to sing. All I have to do is stand up in front of people and explain a couple of sentences."

He stood up very straight, and said in a singsong voice: "Captain Standish mounted the horse. 'Captain Standish' is a proper noun and the subject of the verb 'mounted.' 'The' is an article, an adjective modifying 'horse.' 'Horse' is a noun and the object of the verb."

He made a bow.

"Hooray!" Lionel clapped his hands. He got up and struck a gallant pose. "And I declaim," he said. "I've already memorized my speech."

"And I recite a poem," Horace added.

"But I have to sing," Finley thought bitterly. He began to practice.

Samuel and Horace and Lionel put their hands over their ears. They made terrible faces. Then they began to hum loudly, along with him. They knew they were off key.

Suddenly an idea came to Finley. Hidden

away, under his shirts in the bottom drawer of his chest, was the apple pie Mother had given him. He brought it out.

"M-m-m-m." Horace smacked his lips.

"I will give each of you a piece if you will leave me alone while I practice my song."

"I will," Lionel promised solemnly.

"So will I," said Samuel.

"And I," Horace said.

Finley cut three pieces of pie. He was careful to make them exactly the same size. He gave one to each of his roommates.

"There is more than half the pie left," he told them. "I'll give you all some tomorrow afternoon, too, if you'll leave me alone."

"We will!" cried the boys.

Finley looked at the pie fondly as he wrapped it up. "My peace pie," he said when he put it back in the drawer. "Now I can practice my song in peace."

Exhibition Day dawned bright and clear. Some parents and friends came on horseback and some came on foot. Others came in gigs and chaises. People walked around and through the buildings. They looked over samples of the boys' work, hung on the classroom walls.

Peddlers had set up stands before the buildings. They opened their packs and put out displays. They had ribbons and combs and trinkets of all kinds. There were sweetmeats and gingerbread, too.

Finley wandered among the peddlers' stands. He was happy and confident. His parents would be here any minute. Today he would make them proud of him.

He saw the family gig draw up, and his mother and father get out. He ran to them.

"Good morning, son," his father said heartily. "Are you ready for your part in the program?"

"Oh, yes, sir!"

"We're eager to hear you," said his mother.

"We must go in now and talk to Master Newman about the address I am to make," said Dr. Morse. He and Mrs. Morse went toward the main hall.

It would be a few minutes yet before the exercises began. Finley went back to watch the peddlers for a while longer.

"Have your likeness cut!" a short, dark man was calling. "It takes but five minutes. It costs only twenty-five cents, mounted."

Finley stopped before this display. Here was a way of making likenesses that was new to him.

The man picked up a piece of black paper. With slim scissors he snipped a profile of the lady in front of him. He pasted it on a piece of white paper and handed it to her. Then her husband sat down. The artist cut his likeness out of black paper, too.

Finley edged closer to see the lady's silhouette. He looked from it to her profile. It was a fine likeness. The short, upturned nose was there, and the rounded chin. Even the feather on her bonnet! The likeness of the gentleman was good, too.

Finley watched the snipping scissors as more customers came. After a while the crowd thinned as people went to the exercises.

The man spoke to Finley then. "You've been watching me pretty closely, haven't you?"

"Yes, I have. You cut very good likenesses. I wish I could do it."

"Perhaps you can. Here, try one."

The man pushed a piece of the black paper toward Finley and handed him the scissors. He turned so that Finley could have a side view of his head. "Cut my silhouette," he suggested.

"It should be easy," Finley thought. "He has a big hooked nose and his chin juts out."

128

Finley snipped and snipped. He whacked
here. Then he whacked there. He looked at the
result in disgust. He hadn't come at all close to
a likeness.

The man handed him another piece of paper,
then another and another.

"Practice makes perfect," he said pleasantly. "And I have nothing to do until after the program."

"Program!" Finley cried. His song! He had practiced it so long. And he had wanted to make his parents proud of him.

He dropped the paper and scissors as if they had been hot potatoes. "Thank you!" he called back and ran toward the main hall of Phillips Academy as fast as he could.

As he reached the door his heart sank. The boys' part of the program was over. Father was making his speech!

"You are now laying a foundation for the future," Dr. Morse was saying. "The character and habits you form now will likely continue through life——"

Finley drove home with his parents after the program. Father scolded him all the way.

"You are getting more like Aesop's Hare all

130

the time," he said severely. "You say you learned your song perfectly. Yet when your name was called to sing it, you were outside watching a peddler cut silhouettes. It is fortunate that Master Newman has let you off with demerits. You might have been expelled."

"I'm sorry, Father," Finley replied in a low voice. "Truly I am."

Father was right. He was getting more like the Hare. Always stopping, not to sleep, but to poke his nose into everything along the way.

But that was how he had learned to make silhouettes. Wouldn't Nancy be surprised when he cut her likeness out of black paper! Finley could hardly wait to get home.

Would He Pass?

It was early in the summer of 1805. Fourteen-year-old Samuel Finley Breese Morse sat in his room in the parsonage. His dark head was bent over a piece of paper which he had tacked to a smooth board.

With a piece of charcoal he was drawing a picture of his mother.

Six other pictures of Mrs. Morse were spread out on his bed. In one she was knitting. In another she was reading. In still another she looked out, calmly smiling. Each was different.

"I like this one best," Finley thought, studying the sketch on the board. It was a side view and showed Mrs. Morse wearing her white mob-cap. "The nose is just right. So is the chin."

With a few deft strokes he drew a bow on the front of her cap. "I think I'll use this one in my family group."

He smiled. "Now all I have to do is to get good likenesses of Father and Richard and my-self. I'll use the one I did of Sidney last week. I'll put them all together in one big picture. It should be fun to paint a group of people."

"Finley!" his father called. "Please come to my study. Dr. Dwight is here."

"Yes, Father." Finley had expected his father to call him ever since he had seen the tall, white-haired gentleman get out of his chaise and walk up to the parsonage. Dr. Dwight was President of Yale College, and one of Dr. Morse's friends.

Finley put down his stick of charcoal. He laid the picture beside the other sketches on the bed. Then he washed up and went downstairs.

Sidney came, too.

"I should like to present my sons, Dr. Dwight." Dr. Morse laid an affectionate hand on the shoulder of each boy. "This is Finley and this is Sidney."

The tall gentleman nodded to the boys.

"Boys," Dr. Morse continued, "I have arranged with Dr. Dwight for you to take the entrance examination for Yale this summer. Sidney, you will not enter until next year, but you, Finley, will enter this fall—that is, if you can pass the examination."

"I shall come back late in the summer," Dr. Dwight said, "to give you the examination."

Later, after Dr. Dwight had gone, Dr. Morse motioned Finley back into his study.

He sat down at his desk. "Finley, I am greatly concerned about you. As you know, I was unhappy about your low marks at Phillips. Dr. Dwight was somewhat upset about them, too."

Finley gulped. His marks *had* been low.

His father went on: "You seem to strive for nothing. You are almost a grown man and yet you do not know what career you want to follow when you finish school."

"I want to be a painter," Finley thought. But he knew it would do him no good to say so.

"How unlike your brothers you are! Already they are striving for the ministry." Dr. Morse shook his finger at Finley, but his voice softened. "You have an excellent mind, too, son. I want you to use it and get good marks on your examination. To do that you must review all you studied at Phillips Academy."

"I will, Father," Finley promised solemnly.

Dr. Morse rose. "I know that *now* you intend to, Finley. Your intentions are always good. But good intentions are not enough. You must work and study hard all summer."

Finley went back to his room and headed

straight for the table beside his bed. On it were stacked his books from the academy. He would start studying right away. He must get good marks on that examination.

But as he passed the bed he saw the sketches of his mother. Another idea came to him. "I must get it on paper before I forget it!" he thought.

Soon he was busy on a sketch. "I will put Father here and Mother here, and Sidney and Richard and me around a table." The charcoal flew. Studying was forgotten, and Finley worked on the sketch until suppertime.

FAMILY GROUP

"Richard, hold still!" Finley's voice was sharp. "How can I finish this picture of you before Mother and Father get back if you keep wiggling all the time?"

136

Ten-year-old Richard sighed. "I've been sitting on this old stump all morning. 'Turn this way!' 'Turn that way!' That's all I've heard. I'm tired of turning. I'm tired of sitting here. How many pictures are you going to draw of me, anyway?"

"This is the last one," Finley said. "This one I really like. I'll use it in the family group."

Richard straightened his shoulders and tried to sit as still as a statue. He listened to more scratches of charcoal on paper. He was glad Finley would not keep him much longer.

"When will you finish that family picture, Fin? You've been working on it all summer."

Finley rubbed his nose absent-mindedly. "My charcoal sketch is almost done now. Yours was the last likeness I needed. There, now I have it."

Richard jumped up. "Let me see it!" He ran and peered over Finley's shoulder. "It looks like me all right. But why a side view?"

"You'll see." Finley stood up. "Come, I'll show you."

He picked up the other sketches of Richard and a Latin book which lay beside him.

"You haven't studied your Latin at all," Richard said as he followed Finley into the house.

"I'm going to study it after a while," Finley answered.

In his room he spread out on his bed a large piece of heavy paper. Richard leaned over and gazed at it.

There was the Morse family. Mrs. Morse in her white mobcap, sat at one end of a table. Standing next to her was Sidney, dark-eyed and thoughtful. Dr. Morse, tall and distinguished-looking, was in the center. Finley stood beside him, hand on hip. All were staring at the center of the table.

"Where are you going to put me?" Richard asked.

"At the other end of the table, facing Mother."

"Looking at the middle of the table, too?" asked Richard. "Shouldn't there be something for us to look at?"

Finley rubbed his nose again, leaving a large smudge of charcoal. A lock of dark hair had fallen over his high, broad forehead. He brushed it back, leaving another smudge.

139

"Yes, I have to put some object there," he said. "But I haven't thought of the right thing yet."

"Why not put Father's globe in front of him?" Richard suggested. "He looks at it so often. And he's always showing us places on it."

Finley's eyes lighted up. "Good, Richard!" he cried. "The globe is just the thing!"

He reached for his charcoal and began to sketch. The globe was almost finished when he heard the front door open. Father was home!

At once Finley slipped the family-group picture under the bed, along with the sketches of Richard. He grabbed his Latin book and opened it. When his father came up the stairs he found Finley studying hard.

THE EXAMINATION

One evening in late August the Morse family sat around the dinner table.

"Dr. Dwight is coming tomorrow," Dr. Morse announced quietly. He glanced at Finley and Sidney. "I hope you boys are ready for your examination."

"I am," Sidney said confidently.

Finley stirred uneasily. "I'll study right after dinner tonight," he thought.

He sat up late that night. He studied very hard. "I meant to study this way all summer," he thought with regret. "I wish I really had."

Dr. Dwight came early the next morning. So did Samuel Barrell. He was to take the examination for Yale with the Morse boys.

Dr. Dwight took over Dr. Morse's study. He sat behind the desk. The boys sat at small tables. On each table were paper and a quill pen and an inkwell. The boys were to write down their answers to all the questions.

The examination began. There were questions about Greek grammar, Latin grammar and English grammar. There were problems in arithmetic. There was a composition to write.

Finley tried to concentrate. Each question seemed more difficult than the one before. "If I'd only studied harder this summer," he thought again and again. The hours passed slowly.

At three o'clock Dr. Dwight said, "The examination is over. I will take your papers now."

Finley handed over his papers. His marks would be low, he knew. Would he even pass? That was what worried him now. Father had been right: good intentions were not enough.

Two days later the results of the examination came. Dr. Morse walked into Finley's room, a letter in his hand. "I am disappointed in you, Finley," he said quietly.

Finley felt as if his heart had dropped to the toe of his boot. "Didn't I pass?" he asked.

His father sighed. "Yes, you passed. But I had hoped you would make good marks."

Finley sighed with relief. Now he could work undisturbed on his picture until he left for Yale.

Dr. Morse saw the sketches on the bed. "I suppose you have been working on these when you should have been studying?"

"Yes, sir—I guess so, sir." Finley held up his sketch of the group. "Now I'm going to do a picture like this in color." He frowned. "I can't decide whether to do it in water colors or oils."

His father examined the sketches. He gazed at his own likeness a long time.

Finley watched him expectantly.

"Not too bad," Dr. Morse said at last. "Not too bad—but not too good, either." He put his hand on Finley's shoulder. "You *must* learn to put first things first, Finley. The first thing for you was to pass this examination with credit. Instead, you drew pictures." He turned to leave the room. In the doorway he paused and looked back. "Perhaps Yale will steady you," he said.

Square Peg

Two YOUNG men strolled down the gravel walk that wound among the brick buildings of Yale College. They stopped before one of the dormitories in which the boys lived.

"I've shown you through the buildings," Samuel Barrell said to his companion. "Now you must see the room of my friend Geography Morse. It's a sight no freshman should miss."

Zedekiah Barstow smiled. "You're the third person who has told me that since I came to New Haven. I hear he's quite an artist."

Samuel opened the door. "He certainly is. Come on, his room is down this hall."

144

"Why do they call him Geography?" Zedekiah asked. "His name is Finley, isn't it?"

Samuel shrugged. "His full name is Samuel Finley Breese Morse. We used to call him Finley, but now he wants to be called Samuel. And his nickname is Geography, because of his father's books."

"I really don't care what they call me," a pleasant voice said, "so long as they call me to eat."

Samuel and Zedekiah turned. A tall, dark, blue-eyed boy of sixteen was walking a few steps behind them.

"Geography! You're just the person we're on our way to see. Zedekiah here is a freshman. I want to show him your room."

"Go right ahead," Geography said. "He's welcome to look as long as he likes."

He led the way into a room at the end of the hall. It was very much like all the other dormitory rooms Zedekiah had seen. But unlike the others, the walls of this room were covered from floor to ceiling with pictures.

Zedekiah walked around, admiring them. Most of them were portraits. Some were painted on canvas with oil. Several were on paper, done with water colors. There were a few tiny portraits on ivory, and silhouettes cut from black paper. Others were caricatures, or funny portraits, sketched with charcoal on paper.

Suddenly Zedekiah laughed. He had stopped in front of a large picture that covered almost a whole wall. It was a picture of a mountain labeled THE HILL OF SCIENCE. There were many boys on it—some creeping on their hands and knees, others walking. A few were running. All were trying to reach the top of the hill.

"Isn't that Bill Zincley?" Zedekiah asked. "It's hard for him to get across that ditch!"

He pointed to another figure. "And there's Joseph Dulles. He's almost at the top."

146

Then he noticed, at the foot of the hill, a tired, sleepy-eyed boy. He was trying to crawl over a huge boulder in his path.

"Why, Geography!" Zedekiah laughed. "That's you!"

"And the proper place for me, too," Geography said sadly. "I doubt if I'll ever get over that rock."

The rock was labeled DISLIKE OF STUDY.

"If I had my way," Geography went on, "I'd do nothing but paint."

"Could you paint my portrait?" Zedekiah asked eagerly. "I know my mother would like to have one."

"Certainly. I'll make a sketch right now. Sit down here in the light."

Samuel Barrell left a few minutes later. The sound of charcoal scratching on paper followed him down the hall. Zedekiah was posing for Geography's sketch.

Professor Jeremiah Day stood in front of his class of thirteen boys and announced, "Today we shall begin the study of another subject."

Ho, hum. Samuel Finley Breese Morse could not hold back a yawn. He had sat up late the night before to work on his portrait of Zedekiah Barstow. "I could finish it today," he thought, "if I didn't have to go to classes."

"I shall give a few lectures," Professor Day went on, "on electricity."

Electricity! Samuel's mind snapped to attention. He forgot about the portrait. This was something new. Why, electricity wasn't a subject to study in college! It was a curiosity of nature—though Samuel had to admit that its effects were interesting to watch.

The professor continued: "Man has known a little about electricity for a long time. Many centuries ago the philosophers and scientists of

Greece discovered one way to produce charges of electricity. They also learned some of its properties or characteristics. They saw that, like loadstone, electricity had power to attract objects. However, they were familiar only with electricity at rest—that is, with what is called static electricity."

Samuel remembered the times when his father had talked about electricity. His hand shot up, and the professor nodded. "Is static electricity what causes the sparks you see if you rub a cat's fur," he asked, "or if you rub your shoes on a rug and then touch someone?"

Professor Day nodded again. "Yes," he said, "those are examples of charges of static electricity. Static electricity is caused by the rubbing, or friction, of two substances under the proper conditions. This was the first kind of electricity that man recognized. But only a small charge can be produced in this way.

"About ten years ago," he went on, "an Italian scientist named Alessandro Volta made a great discovery. He discovered that certain combinations of chemicals also produce electricity. This combination of chemicals would produce or generate not just one small charge, like a charge of static electricity, but a steady *flow* or current of charges.

"Volta made a device, which he called a cell, to generate this current. Then he discovered that a group of cells fastened together would generate an even stronger current. He called this group of cells a battery."

Samuel Morse was busy taking notes. He didn't want to forget any of this.

"Now that this power is known," Professor Day said, "who can guess what wonders lie in the future? Someday, perhaps, electricity may even become man's servant and perform useful tasks for him."

Samuel thought, "Why, these wonders may be discovered in my own lifetime!" It was an exciting idea.

Professor Day turned to the table beside him. On it was a strange collection of objects. Samuel could see several glass jars, fastened together by pieces of metal. The jars were filled with acid, the professor said. Each jar was a cell, and they had been fastened together to form a battery. He called the boys up to look at the cells of the battery. When they came closer the boys could see small strips of metal hanging in the acid.

"This is Volta's largest battery," the professor explained. "It generates a strong current of electricity. Later we will build our own battery. But today I want to show you how an electric current moves. May I have two volunteers, to hold these wires of the battery?"

Samuel Morse stepped forward. "I'll hold one, sir!"

Joseph Dulles volunteered also.

"Now, I want you all to stand in a circle around this table and join hands."

He showed Joseph how to grasp the end of one wire, while holding the hand of the boy next to him. The other boys joined hands, around to Samuel, who took hold of the other wire. As he

did so, without warning an electric current flashed around the circle. All the boys felt the shock clearly.

"Ouch!" Joseph dropped his wire. Instantly the current was cut off.

"It felt as though someone had hit my arms with a light blow," Samuel said wonderingly.

"Did you notice that you all felt the shock of the current at exactly the same instant?" asked Professor Day. "You see, the flow begins when a connection is made between the two wires. The current flows from one to the other—that's the circuit of the electricity."

Samuel sat through the rest of the lecture, wide-awake. He was wondering where he could get materials to build a battery.

That night he wrote to his father. Dr. Morse liked to learn about any new scientific discoveries. And he would be glad to know that his oldest son was really interested in one of his classes.

Early in the morning of a summer day four years later Samuel Morse walked slowly down a street in Boston. He was now a young man of twenty.

He stopped, near Scollay Square, at the shop of Daniel Mallory, printer and bookseller. Samuel unlocked the door and went in.

First, he got a broom and swept the floor of the shop. Then, from beneath the counter, he got out a cloth and started to dust books. When a customer came in, Samuel dropped his dust-cloth quickly behind the counter. "Good morning, Mr. Wilson," he said cheerfully. "May I help you?"

"I want your father's geography."

Samuel took a copy of Dr. Morse's book from the shelf.

"How do you like your job?" Mr. Wilson asked in a friendly voice.

"Well, I'm working here to please my father. And the job's all right. But I'd rather work on portraits or my scientific experiments." He sighed. "The things I *like* to do don't help me earn a living."

Mr. Wilson handed him some money. "I hear that Washington Allston has taken an interest in you and your painting. He's a fine artist."

Samuel's face brightened. "Yes, he has. I'm hoping he'll convince my father I should go to London to study."

"How could Allston do that?"

Samuel leaned over the counter. Suddenly he felt that he must share his secret with someone. "Last week," he confided, "I took my two best paintings to him, for his opinion. He asked me to come back tonight. He wants Father to come, also. He's going to tell Father he believes my work shows some talent, and I should study painting abroad."

"Do you think he'll convince your father?"

Samuel looked worried. "There's one bad thing about it. Father knows Mr. Allston is my friend. He may think Mr. Allston will say my work is good only because of our friendship."

Mr. Wilson took his change and package. "Well, the best of luck to you," he said heartily. He liked the polite young bookstore clerk.

"Thank you, sir."

All day long Samuel worked with one eye on the clock. Would the hours never pass?

At last it was time to lock up the shop. Samuel hurried out, straight to Washington Allston's rooms. His father had arrived just a few moments earlier. Allston greeted them warmly.

In the painting room, set up on two easels, were Samuel's pictures. One was a landscape— a peaceful meadow, with great, spreading trees in the distance. The other was a picture of the Pilgrims landing at Plymouth.

Allston wasted no time. He waved toward the easels and said gravely to Dr. Morse, "This is good work. If Samuel were my son I'd send him to London to study. His paintings show real talent, but he needs more training. The great artists who could teach him—men like Benjamin West—are all in London now."

Dr. Morse did not look surprised. "I rather expected you to say something like that," he said quietly.

Samuel's heart sank. Father *did* think Mr. Allston suggested this only because he and Samuel were friends!

There was a rap on the door, and the artist smiled. "So that you wouldn't have to take my opinion alone, I asked someone else to look over the paintings and tell us what he thinks of them."

He went to open the door. "Come in, Mr. Stuart," he said.

In walked a big, handsome man, dressed in

the latest fashion. He was Gilbert Stuart, America's foremost painter!

He had proved that a talented limner could be respectable and successful. Everyone knew his pictures of George Washington. He had painted portraits of important people in New York, Philadelphia and Boston. He had many friends and admirers.

Samuel held his breath. Father would not doubt Gilbert Stuart's judgment about any painting. He couldn't! There was not a better painter in the country.

Mr. Stuart walked over to the easels. He studied Samuel's pictures with piercing eyes. "H-m-m," he murmured at last. "Very interesting. Good use of color."

For several minutes more he studied the paintings. Then he turned to Dr. Morse. "Your son shows considerable talent, though he is untaught. With proper study of anatomy and com-

position, I believe he might develop into a fine painter someday."

Samuel let out his breath with relief. Dr. Morse glanced from one artist to the other. "Thank you, gentlemen, for your advice," he said quietly. "I realize it is based on experience and knowledge."

He turned to his son. "Perhaps, in trying to train you for the ministry," he said, "I've been trying to fit a square peg into a round hole."

He picked up his hat. "I'll see that Samuel gets the money he will need to study in London." He hesitated for a moment, then added, "I'm proud that my son's work has won such high approval."

Wonder of
the World

Dr. Morse kept his word and sent his son to London. There he studied under his friend Washington Allston and under the great Benjamin West. West was the most famous of all American painters and one of the most famous painters in England. By the time he returned to America four years later, Samuel had learned to paint very good pictures.

He opened a small studio in Boston, arranged a show of his pictures, and waited for patrons or customers to come. His father's friends introduced him to some of the city's leading families. But though people praised his work, no one offered to buy a picture or asked him to paint one.

Soon Samuel saw that his father had been right. It was hard for a painter to make a living in the United States. Most people were not wealthy, and few of the wealthy were interested in having pictures painted of themselves or of their families.

Finally Samuel grew discouraged. He closed his studio and went home to Charlestown, across the river.

"Don't worry, son," his father said. "You must expect work to come slowly at first. People must learn who you are and what you can do before you can hope to make a great name for yourself. Go out and meet people and let them see your work. Then you'll get buyers."

By that time summer had come, so Samuel packed his paints and clothes and went to New Hampshire. There were beautiful landscapes there, and prosperous farmers who might be interested in having portraits painted.

In Concord, to his joy, he found his first paying customers. There, too, to his even greater joy, he found a young lady named Lucretia Pickering Walker. Lucretia was beautiful and Samuel fell in love. But her father was wealthy. Samuel was afraid that a struggling artist would have little chance. It took him all summer to get up enough courage to tell her of his feelings. He discovered that Lucretia felt the same way.

He was overjoyed and at the same time almost in despair. He had earned money, but not enough to get married. One day in October, after Mr. Walker had consented to their marriage, Samuel and Lucretia were talking. Samuel was gloomy.

"Unless I can find more sitters, it will be several years before we can marry," he said. "I haven't earned much money yet. Sometimes I think my father was right when he tried to discourage my painting. A painter in America is no better than a beggar."

"Don't be discouraged, Samuel," Lucretia said. "I'm willing to wait a year or two. And I just know that you'll become famous and successful some day."

"I hope you're right," he said, shaking his head sadly. "My uncle has suggested that I go south. There are many rich planters and merchants in South Carolina, he says, who might be interested in having their portraits done."

"It might be wise to go."

"I'll be so far away from you."

"I know," she said. "But if a year there would help you to make a name for yourself and help us to marry, it would be worth while."

"Perhaps I will if things don't improve here," Samuel said.

The fall and winter passed, and things did not improve. Samuel painted several portraits, but he could not earn enough money to support a wife. Finally, in the fall of 1817, he sailed for Charleston, the capital of South Carolina.

There he stayed with his mother's uncle, Dr. Finley, who introduced him to all his friends. Several weeks passed by without orders, and

Samuel grew discouraged again. To pass the time, he painted his uncle's portrait. When people saw it they were amazed by its striking likeness to the doctor. No painter in Charleston had ever been that good.

Suddenly people began flocking to Samuel's studio. Within a few weeks he had enough portraits ordered to keep him busy for months, and all at higher prices than he had received at home.

Samuel was delighted. His dreams and plans soared. "Next fall," he wrote Lucretia, "I shall bring you to Charleston as my wife."

When summer came he returned to Boston with many pictures yet to finish and three thousand dollars in his pocket. There was a flurry of excited preparation in the Walker home in Concord. Then, in September, he and Lucretia were married. A few weeks later they sailed for Charleston.

As their ship left New York, Samuel watched

the city's buildings grow smaller in the distance. Never in his life had he been so happy or so sure of himself. All his dreams seemed finally to be coming true.

"I'll be a great painter yet!" he said, half to himself and half to the rapidly disappearing city. "I know I will!"

"LIGHTNING WOULD SERVE US BETTER"

In 1832 the famous American novelist, James Fenimore Cooper, was living in Paris with his family. His home was a gathering place for the many Americans who were studying in Paris then. One of these Americans was the painter Samuel Finley Breese Morse. Morse had been in Europe since 1829. He had lived in Italy and Switzerland before coming to Paris. He spent many evenings with the Coopers.

One summer night, however, the Coopers had

only one American guest. He was a young art student named Richard Habersham, who shared Samuel Morse's rooms. Richard had really come to see Mr. Cooper's daughter Susan. She was a very pretty young lady, just nineteen. But all through dinner her father and Richard had discussed Cooper's new novel.

After dinner, when they went into the parlor, Cooper said, "I didn't see our friend Samuel in the Louvre today."

"No, sir, he wasn't at the museum today."

"Nor yesterday. I stopped in to tease him about the great picture he is planning."

A servant brought in a coffee tray. Mrs. Cooper asked, "Richard, will you have some coffee with us?"

"If you please, ma'am," he answered politely. He wondered if he would get a chance to talk to Susan. She had sat down in a window seat across the room.

Mrs. Cooper began to pour the coffee. "Poor Mr. Morse," she said. "He's a most unhappy man. His wife's death a few years ago was a hard blow."

"And his painting," added her husband, "hasn't brought him the success he deserves. He's a good artist, but he doesn't get many orders for portraits. He often complains that he can't earn enough to support his children." He glanced anxiously at Richard. "Morse isn't ill, is he, Richard?"

"Oh, no, sir. He's gone out to the country—to study the French semaphore system!"

"What in the world is that?" asked Susan.

Her father threw back his head and laughed. "I should have guessed Morse had a new interest! Why, Susan, that's telegraphy—a system of sending messages in code by signals. You've seen some of the semaphores on hills. They're tall wooden posts, with 'arms' that move up or down. These movements can be seen on hills far away. And if Morse is interested in the semaphore now, I suppose he thinks of nothing else."

Richard smiled. "Mr. Morse is always talking about different ways to send messages—under water, over wires, and so on. I guess I've heard him tell a hundred times how news of the opening of the Erie Canal was sent eastward along the canalway."

"So have we," said Cooper, while his wife and daughter nodded. "Yet I admit it's interesting. A signal passed along by cannon shots—another fired as the sound of a distant shot reached it—that's a kind of telegraphy, too, Susan."

She had been listening quietly, looking out the window. Suddenly she cried, "Oh, Mr. Morse is coming down the street."

Mrs. Cooper smiled. "I suppose we shall now learn all about the semaphore."

A few minutes later Samuel Morse was sitting

in the Cooper's parlor. He was still a handsome man, though he was now forty-one and his dark hair was gray at the temples.

Mrs. Cooper poured some coffee for him. Richard moved over to the window seat to chat with Susan. James Fenimore Cooper began to tease his friend about neglecting his painting.

"That's true," Morse said seriously. "I haven't been at the Louvre all week." He took a sip of the steaming coffee. "Mrs. Cooper, this is delicious coffee."

As she smiled at him, he went on: "One of the French officials heard that I was studying their semaphores. He invited me to inspect this tele-graph system. It was an interesting experience."

"Do you think the telegraph will take the place of mails?" asked Cooper.

Samuel Morse hardly noticed that Mrs. Cooper had refilled his cup. He was eager to talk. "No, for long messages the mails will al-

ways be best. But for short messages the semaphore is certainly faster. It might be even better
in America, where there is less fog."

He drank his second cup of coffee. "But the
semaphore," he continued, "can't be seen at

173

night or in bad weather. In my opinion, the system isn't fast enough, anyway. Lightning would serve us better! It could be seen at night, too," he added with a smile.

The others laughed.

"Oh, Samuel, a serious artist shouldn't dream of sending messages on the wings of lightning!" said Cooper. "By the way, when do you expect to finish the picture of the Louvre gallery that you've been working on?"

"I still have several paintings to copy. I decided to show fifty of the Louvre masterpieces in my big picture. I'll finish it at home, but I must have copies of all fifty paintings before I sail."

Morse put his cup on a table and leaned back in his chair. "I've been copying the 'Mona Lisa.' I marvel at the man who painted her. To think that an artist as great as Leonardo da Vinci was also an inventor!"

James Fenimore Cooper smiled. "I'm not surprised. You've done a bit of inventing yourself, haven't you?"

"You mean my fire-engine pump and my marble-carving machine?" Morse sighed. "Neither was very successful." Then he brightened. "But a lightning-fast telegraph, which would work perfectly at any time in any weather —*that* would be the wonder of the world!"

A VOYAGE OF DISCOVERIES

On a windy day in October, Samuel Morse boarded the packet *Sully*. She was a small vessel which carried mail across the Atlantic Ocean. Like many mail boats, she carried a few passengers as well.

Two families and three other gentlemen were, like Morse, returning to America. Captain Pell introduced Morse to Mr. Fisher, a Philadelphia lawyer. "And this is Dr. Jackson, of Boston," the captain said as he presented a third passenger. "He has been studying science in Paris."

"At least I'll have interesting companions on the voyage home," thought Morse.

But the voyage did not begin at once. The winds shifted, and for a week the *Sully* lay windbound in the harbor at Le Havre. There was nothing for the passengers to do but eat, walk the decks and talk. Morse enjoyed the long conversations.

One day at lunch Dr. Jackson began to tell about a Frenchman he had met, named Ampère. He described Ampère's work to prove that electricity and magnetism were related.

"And now there's some device called an electromagnet," Mr. Fisher said. "I've heard it may lead to great scientific advances."

Morse, who sat next to him, nodded. "Yet it's a simple thing—just a piece of soft iron, with wire coiled around it. It's magnetic only while electric current flows through that coil. Then it's so much stronger than a natural magnet that it can move much heavier objects. But its power can always be controlled by the current."

"You know a good deal about it," said Mr. Fisher in surprise.

"I've always been interested in electricity," Morse explained. "I've heard lectures about the electromagnet. I try to keep up with all the new developments."

"Tell me something," Mr. Fisher said. "Is an electric current slowed up when it travels over a very long wire?"

"Oh, no," Dr. Jackson answered quickly. "It passes along a wire instantly, no matter how long the wire is."

"That's so," said Samuel Morse. He looked very thoughtful. "If an electric current can travel instantly, even to a point far away, then perhaps a way can be found to send signals instantly over long distances. Not only signals—whole messages! They could be recorded, too!" He struck the table with one hand. "And before this voyage is over I believe I can work out the way to do it. Gentlemen, your talk has given me a great idea!"

In his excitement, Morse had forgotten to eat. Now, forgetting even to excuse himself, he sprang up and rushed out on deck. The other passengers stared after him in amazement.

Outside, Morse began to pace up and down the deck of the *Sully*. In his imagination he could see the very instruments needed to send and record signals. At last he went to his cabin and took a blank notebook from his trunk. He began to scribble. He filled page after page with notes and sketches.

For several days and nights he worked on his ideas. Finally he showed the notebook with all its sketches and notes to Dr. Jackson.

"I've drawn up plans for an *electric* telegraph system," he said proudly. "And its beauty lies in its simplicity. There are just three parts—a sender, the circuit through which the electric current flows, and a receiver. With these, any message can be sent by signals, and written down as it comes in."

He pointed to one of his sketches. "Here's the sender, attached to this battery. It's just a metal bar. I call it a key, because it opens and closes the circuit. The current flows through a wire from the battery to the receiver. The wire could be laid underground, in a clay tube, or perhaps strung up on wooden posts in the air."

Dr. Jackson studied the sketch. "But how will you record the signals?"

"That's where I use the electromagnet. See this other bar, or lever, near it?" Morse asked. "When the current flows, the electromagnet is strong enough to attract one end of the lever.

179

That forces the other end down. A pencil attached there will leave a mark on a roll of paper, unwinding slowly beneath it. Then, when the current is cut off, the electromagnet loses its power. The lever falls back and the pencil comes up."

"You say it will make a mark on the paper?" Dr. Jackson asked, puzzled.

"A number of marks, really, as the current goes on and off. Messages will be sent in a code, of course. I've worked out a code made up of dots and dashes. Different combinations of dots and dashes stand for different numbers or letters of the alphabet."

"How can you send two kinds of signals?"

Morse explained patiently, "You press the key of the sender down for a moment. When you lift your finger, the current is cut off. But with that brief charge the pencil has been forced down, and made a dot. If you press the key longer, the charge will last longer, and the pencil will leave a dash."

"H-m-m," murmured Dr. Jackson admiringly. "Very clever. I begin to understand."

Samuel Morse closed his notebook. "As soon as we dock, I'll start to build models of my sender and receiver." He turned to Captain Pell, who was coming along the deck. "If you hear of Morse's electric telegraph or Morse's code someday, you can remember the discoveries were made on board your good ship *Sully!*"

"What Hath God Wrought?"

ON MAY 24, 1844, Samuel Morse sat in the Supreme Court chamber in the Capitol in Washington, D.C. A working model of his electric telegraph was on a table in front of him.

The telegraph line between Washington and Baltimore, Maryland, was completed. Morse's friend and partner, Alfred Vail, sat in Baltimore before another model of the telegraph. Between the two instruments were miles of wire. It was strung on poles along the railroad tracks that ran from one city to the other.

Many Congressmen and important government officials had come to watch the test.

"We'll soon see," said one Senator, "whether Congress has spent $30,000 on a gimcrack."

The Senator next to him smiled. "Well, Morse waited a long time for the money to build this line. He gave demonstrations of his instruments and pleaded for six years."

"But if the electric telegraph works," a Representative answered, "it will be a boon to mankind. Imagine sending a message and receiving an answer in a matter of minutes!"

"Even the fastest mail could never equal it," said the first Senator. "Look, there goes Miss Annie Ellsworth. She handed Mr. Morse a slip of paper. I suppose the message is written on it."

A tall man, a stranger to the Senators, was sitting back of them. He leaned forward and asked, 'Why was that young lady chosen to give the first message?"

"Her father is the Commissioner of Patents," one of the Senators answered. "Mr. Morse gave

184

her the honor because she was the first to tell him Congress had voted funds to build his telegraph line. The bill was passed at midnight, just before Congress adjourned. Morse had given up all hope and had gone to his hotel. It seems Mr. Ellsworth told his daughter. She rushed over to the hotel the next morning to tell Mr. Morse the news."

"He's reading the message now," the gentleman said. "I wonder what it is."

"We'll find out when it comes back—*if* it comes back!"

The door to the chamber was closed. Samuel Morse looked down at his telegraph instruments. There was a key with which to send the message to Baltimore. Beside it was the receiver, with a big roll of paper attached. Morse placed his finger on the key and tapped out the message.

Then he waited. Most of the men kept their eyes on their watches. The chamber was so quiet one could have heard a pin drop. Had Alfred Vail received the message in Baltimore? The waiting became unbearable.

Click, cli-i-ick, cli-i-ick; click—— The lever began to flash back and forth. By clockwork the roll of paper moved. As if by magic, dots and dashes appeared on it.

Samuel Morse was smiling. When the lever stopped, he translated the code on the paper into words. Proudly he handed the strip of paper to Miss Ellsworth.

"It's the same message!" she cried. Solemnly she read aloud: "What hath God wrought?"

The audience broke into excited talk and applause. They pressed forward to congratulate the inventor.

"That message traveled to Baltimore and back in less than two minutes!" one Senator exclaimed. "Now we know we didn't spend money on a gimcrack!"

The electric telegraph changed slightly after Samuel Morse sent the famous message to Baltimore. Operators discovered they could understand Morse code by listening to the clicks. A "sounder" was invented and added to the receiver to make the clicks louder. Now the operators listened and wrote down the messages as they came in. They learned to translate the code into words as they wrote. They did not need to wait for the receiver to record the dots and dashes.

On June 10, 1871, a convention in New York City was drawing to a close. Telegraph operators from all over the United States and Canada were there. They had gathered to honor the "Father of the Telegraph"—Samuel F. B. Morse. If it had not been for Morse's work on the telegraph, not one of them would have had the job he had.

A statue had been unveiled that afternoon in

Central Park. Throngs of people had cheered as the flag slipped from the bronze likeness of the man they honored.

That evening three young men were making their way to the Music Hall on Fourteenth Street. They were all telegraphers. Thad Moses had come from San Francisco, Bob Simpson from New Orleans. Henry Thomas lived in New York City.

"Say, that was a handsome statue, wasn't it?" Thad said, as they walked along.

Bob, a tall, lanky fellow, nodded. "I'm glad I gave my dollar to the fund that was collected to have it made."

"So am I," Henry Thomas said. "I heard that every telegrapher in the Union, and many in Canada and all over the world gave a bit."

"Too bad Mr. Morse couldn't be at the unveiling this afternoon," Bob commented.

"He's eighty years old now, and probably

can't stand much excitement. He'll be at the reception tonight, though," said Thad. "And there will be a ceremony when he sends a message."

"It'll be interesting to see the inventor of the telegraph operate a key just as we do every day," Henry said. "I wonder whether he remembers his Morse code!"

Bob laughed. "He should if anybody does! He invented the code as well as the telegraph."

They reached the Music Hall and joined the crowd pressing inside.

"There's Samuel Morse!" Thad Moses pointed to an old, white-haired, white-bearded man sitting on the stage.

"That's Cyrus Field beside him," Henry said. "He and Morse laid the Atlantic cable so that telegraph messages could be sent all the way to Europe under the water.

"I see Horace Greeley and Henry Ward Beecher," he added. "And there's our boss,

President Orton of the Western Union Company—the man handing a scroll to Morse."

"That must be the list of everyone who contributed to the fund for the statue of Mr. Morse," Bob said.

Henry nodded. "I heard that the list was nineteen feet long."

At last the hour of nine o'clock came. The speeches were over. It was time for Samuel Morse to send his message to the world.

A telegraph instrument was brought on the stage. It was just like the one used twenty-seven years before. A pretty young lady sat down at the key. Samuel Morse handed her a slip of paper on which his message was written. The girl began tapping out the words in Morse code: *Dash, dash, dot; dot—dot, dot; dot——*

She completed the message, and Morse sat down in her place. The old man put his finger on the key and added: *Dot, dot, dot; dot, dash,*

dot; dash, dot, dot, dot; dash, dash; dot—dot;
dot—dot, dot; dot, dot, dot; dot.

. . .   . — .   — . . .   — —   . .   . .

Listening closely, the telegraphers of course could understand the familiar Morse code. The inventor's message was: "Greetings and thanks to the telegraph fraternity throughout the world. Glory to God in the highest, on earth peace, good will to men." What he had added was: "S. F. B. Morse."

More About This Book

WHEN SAMUEL F. B. MORSE LIVED

1791   SAMUEL F. B. MORSE WAS BORN, APRIL 27.

There were fourteen states in the Union.

The population of the country was about 4,060,000.

George Washington was President.

1791–   SAMUEL GREW UP IN AND AROUND CHARLES-
1810   TOWN, MASSACHUSETTS.

First electric storage battery was developed, 1800.

The United States bought the Louisiana Territory from France, 1803.

Lewis and Clark explored the Northwest, 1804–1806.

1810–   SAMUEL STUDIED PAINTING IN ENGLAND.
1815
James Madison was President, 1809–1817.

The War of 1812 was fought, 1812–1815.

First account of the Lewis and Clark Expedition was published, 1814.

1815– MORSE WORKED AS A PORTRAIT PAINTER.
1832
The first steamship crossed the Atlantic, 1819.

Joseph Henry made the first successful electromagnet, 1830.

Peter Cooper built the first steam locomotive
in the United States, 1830.

Cyrus McCormick invented the reaper, 1831.

1832– MORSE INVENTED THE FIRST ELECTRIC TELE-
1844   GRAPH AND WORKED TO PERFECT IT.
American settlers reached Oregon, 1836.

Texas won independence from Mexico, 1837.

William Henry Harrison became President and
died, 1841.

1844– MORSE DEMONSTRATED HIS ELECTRIC TELE-
1872   GRAPH AND HELPED TO PUT IT INTO USE.
The Mexican War was fought, 1846–1848.

The War between the States was fought, 1861–
1865.

The first transcontinental telegraph was completed, 1861.

The first transatlantic cable was successfully
laid, 1866.

194

There were thirty-seven states in the Union.

The population of the country was about
39,720,000.

Ulysses S. Grant was President.

DO YOU REMEMBER?

1. Where did Samuel Finley Breese Morse live, and what did his father do?

2. What did Finley discover one day when he was rubbing his cat?

3. Why did Ma'am Rand pin Finley's shirt to her dress one day at school?

4. How did Finley find out what caused sparks when he walked over the rug?

5. Why did Finley's father take him to see the artist, Mr. Philip Poole?

6. What did Mr. Poole demonstrate to Finley by rubbing a glass rod with silk?

7. Why did Dr. Morse compare Sidney and Finley with the Tortoise and the Hare?

8. How did Finley find out how to read the invisible message that Billy wrote him?

9. Why did Finley almost fail at Phillips Academy?

10. How did Finley demonstrate to his friends at Yale College that he could paint?

11. How did Finley learn about electricity and storage batteries at Yale?

12. How did Morse manage after many disappointments to become a successful painter?

13. How did Morse happen to plan an electric telegraph on the way home from France?

14. What famous message did Morse use to demonstrate his electric telegraph to Congress?

15. What great celebration was held for Morse in New York when he was eighty years old?

IT'S FUN TO LOOK UP THESE THINGS

1. What kind of school was Phillips Academy, which Finley attended as a boy?

2. What is a portrait painter and how does he differ from other painters?

3. How were messages sent in the early days of our country when Finley was a boy?

4. What did Benjamin Franklin find out about lightning with his famous kite experiment?

5. Who were Ampere and Volta and what did they discover about electricity?

6. How did Alexander Graham Bell use electricity in inventing the telephone?

7. How widely is the electric telegraph used today?

INTERESTING THINGS YOU CAN DO

1. Collect copies of paintings by Morse and prepare an exhibit on the bulletin board.

2. Make a list of famous artists who are known throughout the world for their paintings.

3. Draw a silhouette, or side view, of one of your friends using a pencil or crayon.

4. Make a simple telegraph set, following the directions in an elementary science book.

5. Find a copy of the Morse code and use it to write a message.

6. Read about the laying of the first Atlantic cable and give a report to the class.

7. Obtain a telegraph blank and demonstrate how telegrams are written.

OTHER BOOKS YOU MAY ENJOY READING

All About Famous Inventors and Their Inventions, Fletcher Pratt. Random House.

James Fenimore Cooper: Leatherstocking Boy, Gertrude Hecker Winders. Trade and School Editions, Bobbs-Merrill.

Little Giant of Schenectady, Dorothy Markey. Trade Edition, Dutton. School Edition, American Book.

Medals for Morse, Jean Lee Latham. Trade Edition, Dutton. School Edition, American Book.

Messages, Men, and Miles, Robert Wells. Prentice.

Tom Edison: Boy Inventor, Sue Guthridge. Trade and School Editions, Bobbs-Merrill.

INTERESTING WORDS IN THIS BOOK

amber (ăm'bẽr) : yellowish or brownish stonelike substance, easily electrified

Ampere (äm pâr') : French scientist who made important discoveries in electricity

apothecary (*a* pŏth'ĕ kẽr'ĭ) : person who prepares and sells drugs, a druggist

boom: long wooden beam used for lifting

198

chaise (shāz) : covered two-wheeled carriage usually drawn by one horse

chimney sweep: person who cleans soot from chimneys

coat of arms: emblem or shield of a family

cobblestones: rounded stones used in paving streets

code: system of signals or signs used in sending messages

common: land that the people of a community own and use together, as a park

concentrate (kŏn'sĕn trāt) : center or fix attention on, think carefully about something

corridor (kŏr'ĭ dôr) : hall or passageway

crestfallen: dejected, downhearted, disappointed

declaim (dḗ klām') : speak, recite

deft: skillful

distract: divert or turn aside

dormitory (dôr'mĭ tō'rĭ) : building where students live at a boarding school, also a room containing several beds

edition (ḗ dĭsh'ŭn) : all copies of a book, magazine, or newspaper printed at one time

expelled: forced or asked to leave

frivolous (frĭv'ȯ lŭs) : carefree, lighthearted

gig: light two-wheeled carriage drawn by one horse

gristmill: mill for grinding grain

invisible (ĭn vĭz′ĭ b′l) : cannot be seen

jet: lustrous black

mobcap: woman's cap, often trimmed with frills or ruffles, fastened under the chin

mortar (môr′tẽr) : strong hollow vessel in which things are pounded or ground with a pestle

parsonage: residence of a parson or minister

pestle (pĕs′l) : instrument with rounded end used to pound or grind things in a mortar

pewter (pū′tẽr) : mixture of tin and copper

profile (prō′fīl) : side view of a person's head

salvation (săl vā′shŭn) : saving from sin

sapling: young tree

scroll (skrōl) : roll of paper containing a message, usually honoring someone or something

silhouette (sĭl′ōō ĕt′) : profile of a person's head, done in a solid color

specimen (spĕs′ĭ mĕn) : sample

thong: strip of leather used for tying something

Vinci, Leonardo da (dä Vēn′chĕ) : famous Italian painter and scientist

200